A SPOONFUL
OF HONEY

PIERRE LEYSEN

THE SISTERS OF THE VISITATION

ROCK ISLAND, ILL.

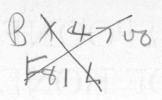

Imprimatur:

✠ Joseph H. Schlarmann,
Bishop of Peoria

October 23, 1947.

Printed by Watkins Printing Company
Baltimore, Md.

TO MY FATHER

"More flies are caught with a spoonful of honey than with a barrel of vinegar".

St. Francis de Sales

TABLE OF CONTENTS

Chapter I

A SINGLE YELLOW ROSE

BRILLIANT! That was the word they used. The marriage ceremonial, ever-ancient, ever-new, was lovely as always. The crowds, however, took that for granted. What they discussed for days on end, the elite over their cups of wine "with beaded bubbles winking at the brim," the peasants stooping and struggling amid the purpling grapes and leafy vines, was the sheer brilliance of the match. On that morning in early April, a day indeed strayed in from summer, two well-known, distinguished families had been united by the marriage of Frances de Sionnas, daughter of Melchior de Sionnas, Lord of Thuille, Vallieras and Boisy, and Francis de Sales, Lord of Nouvelles, who assumed upon his marriage to the charming maiden the title of Lord of Boisy.

The dowry Milchior's daughter gave her husband consisted not only in vast wealth, but also of a name famous for centuries in French history. Indeed, the family proudly traced their descent from a ruler no less than Charlemagne, mightiest of the mighty French rulers! On the bridegroom's side there was an ancient affinity between the House of Sales and that of the illustrious Bernard of Clairvaux. Could two more noble families be united?

* * *

The newly-delegated Lord of Boisy, tall, blue-eyed and fair, former Page to Prince Francis of Luxemburg, and ranking officer in the Duc d'Etampes' cavalry regiment, was walking slowly up and down one of the wide promenades bordering Lake Geneva. By his side was his charming and comely wife, scarcely more than a girl, whose grace, modesty, and poise were the admiration of all. Her greatest asset, however, was her clear, limpid, gray eyes that told of beauty of soul that matched that of body.

Scarcely a month had the two been married. Everything was new, lovely, breath-taking! Now their sojourn at Lake Geneva was nearly ended; the official business Monsieur de Boisy had been sent to transact for Emmanuel Philbert, Duke of Savoy, was nearing completion. Soon the radiantly happy bride and groom would return to the busy, work-a-day world of Thorens and its neighborhood.

"Does the sunset, my lord, seem more colorful here at Geneva, than in our beloved France?"

questioned Frances as she paused to gaze at the changing heavens.

Captivated by the lovely scene, her husband stayed his steps. Pink and white clouds were lightly drifting across the evening sky in graceful laziness. In the distance in all their savage splendor, the Alps, snow-capped and mantled and shod, rose to prodigious heights.

"My darling wife," gently answered her fond husband, "God has indeed given us a tender expression of His fatherly love. This evening's sunset is far more dazzling than any I have ever seen."

"Even the lake," continued Frances, "is a mass of iridescent colors in the glow of the setting sun. Look! Is there any artist comparable to the Divine Creator? How can anyone ever doubt that there is a God?"

"Perhaps, my dear," remarked the young lord, "this is the one time when you and I together can breathe the celestial fragrance of the flower of immortality."

"What is that?" asked Frances with puzzled eyes.

"Have you never heard the story that when Paradise was lost to Adam and Eve, an angel cut and saved a single, beautiful, yellow rose? Sooner or later, at sometime or another in each mortal's life, and at only one time, one breath of perfume from the immortal rose is given to each person, good or bad, rich or poor, high-born or low-born. As I just suggested, it might be that you and I in this enchanting Swiss city are enjoying our share of this lovely flower."

"Where, Francis, did you learn this delightful legend?"

"From an old French soldier who, having seen service in Mesopotamia, likely picked up the tale in the valley of the Euphrates. He told it to us the night before the siege of St. Didier. Its effect upon us was like martial music — it stimulated our courage, made us eager to live to find the flower — and, naturally, we won the next day's battle."

"How charming, really charming," exclaimed the young bride, her eyes glowing in appreciation at the lovely tale. "Shall we rest here on this rustic bench and feast our eyes and steep our souls in this beauty? It is sad there are no others around to enjoy this evening's splendor."

"My dear wife," said the solicitous husband, "let me fold this cape over your shoulders; the night air is already growing cooler. See afar off the birds are circling ever higher 'in the purple twilight of the setting sun.' What beauty!"

"Dear Francis, perhaps our sweet happiness these

few weeks is a precious harbinger of many glorious years ahead, cup-filled and running over with joys."

"What the future holds for us, my cherished Frances, is undoubtedly a sealed book. I, however, fervently hope that God, in His own good time, will send us many sons and daughters; sons who will gain fame as courtiers, soldiers and lawyers, in a few words, worthy descendants of their noble ancestors; daughers, fair, virtuous and lovely, patterned closely after their own estimable mother, the sweetest of Savoy's charming maids."

As Francis uttered these tender words his head rested lightly on his wife's breast. There was a short pause before he spoke again. "Frances, I have been listening to your heart beats. Let me tell you what I just heard: My God, I love you. My God, I thank you for giving me my beloved husband. May we live truly Christian lives, never losing sight of our eternal destiny. May we be together with You, throughout the blessed twilight hours of eternity."

Frances, starry-eyed, answered, "How did you know the prayer in my heart? Those are almost my very words."

She did not, however, tell her husband a tiny, but magnificent petition he had failed to hear, a prayer that someday they might have the distinctive happiness of givng a son to God in holy religion. Frances was really wise beyond her years. She knew that her husband, though an excellent Catholic, was not interested in raising sons for the priesthood. Why mar a perfect evening by starting an argument?

* * *

One of the warmest days in August was slowly drawing to a close. Already the little world, comprising the estates of Monsieur and Madame de Boisy was wrapped in solemn stillness. The old chateau itself, built about the year one thousand, with its six high towers and three small ones, was quiet, hushed and dark, except for two lights which cast faint gleams from the room of St. Francis Assisi. Within this tiny room life and death were struggling.

Madame de Boisy's first child had just been born prematurely that night of the twenty-first, and the lives of both mother and child were endangered. Grave anxiety etched the faces of all in the room; Frances de Boisy alone remained calm and unperturbed, her confidence in God unshaken. Again and again the words of the psalmist, learned long ago at her mother's knee, flitted through her mind. While those around her prayed, she thought:

"They that trust in the Lord shall be as Mount

Sion: he shall not be moved forever that dwelleth in Jerusalem.

The hills stand round about her: even so the Lord is round about His people from this time forth forevermore.

The Lord will not leave the rod of sinners over the lot of the just: that the just may not stretch forth their hands unto them that are of right heart. . . . . ."

Then Frances recalled those encouraging words of happiness promised to the just servants of the Lord:

"Blessed are all they that fear the Lord, that walk in His ways.

For thou shalt eat the labors of thy hands: blessed art thou, and it shall be well with thee.

Thy wife shall be a fruitful vine on the walls of thy house.

Thy children as olive plants, round about thy table.

Behold, thus shall the man be blessed that feareth the Lord."

The next day was one filled with glorious sunshine. The young mother had gradually fallen asleep during the short hours of the summer night and the first pearly streaks of dawn found her rested and strengthened, but not so her baby.

"Let us have him baptized at once," exclaimed the harassed father as he gazed in anguish on his tiny, delicate heir.

Arrangements were quickly completed. Dom Francois de la Flechere, prior of the Benedictine Monastery of Sillingy, was to be the child's godfather, while Madame de Boisy's mother was chosen as godmother. Monsieur de Boisy, proud but fearful, carefully carried his precious son, gently wrapped in linens and resting in his little cradle, down the narrow, dusty road, transformed into a carpet of gold by the warm, bright rays of the mid-August sun. The little parish church of St. Maurice at Thoren was about three leagues distant from Annecy. Scarcely had the saving waters of the holy sacrament been poured over the infant's head, and the name Francis been pronounced, than the assisting curate and a number of those present noticed that the child was beginning to evidence marked signs of new vigor and of grace.

What a glorious homecoming! Such universal rejoicing! How the delighted mother caressed the newly-made heir of heaven! Little did the majority of those who participated in the happy event that twenty-second day of August, 1567, realize that they had just witnessed the christening of one who was to become one of the greatest saints of all ages and climes.

Tall glowing tapers, rich masses of fleur-de-lis, heavy silver dishes all graced the laden table to which Monsieur de Boisy led the noble company of guests who had honored the baptism of his heir.

In the midst of pleasant eating and genial toasting the new father was mindful of the poor who rejoiced with him but could not be invited to the feast. Calling Jacques, one of the servers to him, he whispered, "See that all our tenants have extra food and drink this noon and evening. Tell Pierre Pinquot to give alms to all comers at the chateau gate until midnight."

"Yes, Monsieur," replied the obsequious retainer, whose honey-brown features spoke more eloquently than words of the happiness welling up in his heart because his gracious master had his heart's desire — an heir.

* * *

Francis, so-named not because of his parents, but in honor of the gentle Seraph of Assisi, developed slowly but surely, into a staunch and sturdy lad, under the watchful care of his nurse, Madame de Monthoux who regarded her youthful charge as the apple of her eye. During these early formative years Francis managed to get into enough innocent mischief to prove that he was thoroughly human, culpable and lovable with a decided weakness for sweets, pretties and novelties. Many are the intimate and delightful anecdotes concerning his boyhood.

On one occasion he paid a most informal visit to the warm, delicious-smelling kitchen, presided over by a veritable Sybarite who knew that the young lord of the chateau was strickly forbidden to enter her domain. Pastries had just been baked. The temptation was too strong for Francis. His eloquent blue eyes pleaded for some. In a spirit of mischief, the cook placed two scalding hot cakes in his out-stretched hands. How they burned! Hiding the sharp tears that flooded his eyes he hastily fled to his room where he eventually devoured the goodies. Alas, his poor fingers were nearly raw. Seeking his beloved mother in her boudoir, and finding her doing needle-point, he threw himself at her knees and meekly confessed his fault of disobedience, displaying his stinging, red hands. Madame de Boisy gazed at her kneeling son, his beautiful golden curls tossed and tumbled, and thought of the Infant Samuel, and lightly kissing his serious brow, wisely made no comment, but quietly dressed the painful burns.

Almost as soon as Francis could speak his father

had engaged an excellent priest, M. Jean Deage, to teach his son his first prayers and the elements of Christian Doctrine. Madame de Boisy, too, took her turn in instructing. Both found the lad an apt, brilliant and talented pupil, with a precocious memory.

How often "the child is father of the man"! As soon as Francis had mastered a certain number of questions and answers, he hastened to share his knowledge. Taking a little bell, a gift treasured from babyhood, he would hurry around the neighborhood, summoning his companions to his home for their weekly lesson on God. Arranging the little group around him he would proceed to teach them the lessons he had so eagerly learned. Jacques, Jean, Pierre and Louis, all from nearby estates, earnestly and carefully memorized the answers their little catechist so painstakingly taught. All, however, did not take so kindly to Francis' methods. One evening, Monsieur de Petrie, a Calvinist, was a guest at the chateau. Francis, at the advanced age of five, decided to catechize him. After two or three questions which the elderly gentleman answered according to the Huguenot belief, Francis undertook the task of showing him the errors of his doctrine. Monsieur de Petrie, growing red with chagrin and excitement, glanced from host and hostess to their son, thinking that the lad had been instigated to cross-question him. Madame de Boisy, noticing the guest's embarrassment, suggested that it was past Francis' bedtime, and the lad, always well-mannered, bade a cheerful and courteous goodnight to the guest, thus, more or less, managing to make him forget his discomfort. After that unpleasant experience, both Madame and Monsieur de Boisy saw that the little missionary was securely quartered in his own room when any Huguenots were guests at the chateau.

As the days clustered into weeks, and weeks flitted in months, Francis frequently accompanied his good mother on visits to the poor of the neighborhood. Realizing that example is more powerful than precept, Madame de Boisy so impressed her son with the potent, far-reaching effects of good deeds that many years later, as Bishop and Prince of the church, he was to be known as the great Apostle of charity, to whom God's poor never appealed in vain.

It happened during one of these neighborly visits, that Madame de Boisy noticed her son's pockets were unusually round and bulgy. She said nothing, thinking that he had probably gathered a large quantity of chestnuts which were found in such abundance in that part of the country.

Upon entering the first cottage, Madame de Boisy was astonished to see her son pull a large, bulky package out of his pocket.

"Will you have some peaches?" he asked, approaching the wizened peasant who was husking corn by her fire.

The old lady's beady eyes sparkled; already her lips were smacking in keen anticipation of the extraordinary treat—fresh, smooth, golden-flecked peaches in late fall! Greedily she selected two of the largest, a trifle bruised from cramped quarters, and quickly bit into the luscious fruit.

Francis' mother, deeply touched, said nothing while she admired the brave spirit that had moved him to give away his own share of his favorite hothouse peaches.

As he grew older, Francis was blessed with five younger brothers and two sisters (Gallois, Louis, John Francis, Bernard, Jarus, Gasparde and Jeanne), though the youngest girl, Jeanne, lived only until she reached her early teens. The oldest lad might easily have made himself leader in all those numerous, delightful games of childhood. Strange, but nevertheless natural in one of his disposition, Francis cared little for these pastimes. He, like his name-sake, Francis of Assisi, much preferred to enjoy the beauties of birds and flowers.

Bees making honey, the two-hearted Paghlagonian partridge, lambs, fair and mottled, the voice of the turtle dove, the little spring violet "hidden amid the large leaves of its lowliness, spreading around unequal sweetness," the velvety rose "more pleasing when it is fresh, more fragrant when it is dry," all, each and all, raised his mind to the heavenly Artificer and gave the observant lad food for thought for many, many future conferences.

Chapter II

WILD, PURPLE FOXGLOVES

"FIRST we learn to read, then we read to learn." Francis, even before he was sent to school at the age of seven, showed a pronounced liking for books. He enjoyed caressing the rich bindings, fingering the smooth pages and trying to puzzle out the printed letters.

It was quite against the wishes of Madame de Boisy that her son was sent at such a tender age into the miniature world of the school-room. Monsieur de Boisy, however, overruled her objections by stressing the fact that Madame d'Ecrue, at whose home Francis was to board, was a most excellent Christian and had, herself, raised eight boys. Then, too, from time to time, Francis could easily visit his parents as their chateau was only three leagues distant from La Roche where the college was located.

Repeated rounds of lessons easily learned marked the two years that the young boy spent in his first hall of learning, French and Latin, work and prayer, each and all received due attention as Fran-

cis found exquisite music in his daily work and
melody in the flowers which flourished so profusely
in the college gardens. All unnecessarily had Monsieur de Boisy counseled Pierre Batailleur, one of
La Roche's pedagogues, to keep a watchful eye on
Francis.

In 1576 the de Boisy family, for political reasons,
left their home in Thorens for the chateau de Brens
in the Chablais. Francis was immediately enrolled
at the college of Annecy, with M. Deage accompanying him as guardian. Here one of the lad's
first activities, after he had been duly installed in
the college, was to erect a tiny oratory in his room,
similar to the shrines he had built in his former
home.

"Now," he exclaimed happily to his cousin and
fellow-student, Louis de Sales, "We can have our
little novenas to Our Lord and His saints. Never,
Louis, shall we find our studies too difficult if we
kneel here to pray for light and grace."

Frequently during the next five years the clear,
silver tinkle of a tiny bell announced to Francis'
companions that a procession in honor of the Child
Jesus, or a novena to the Virgin Mother was about
to begin. Eagerly and quickly, books and quills
were set aside as the lads, without exception, cheerfully answered Francis' summons. Never was one

word of disparagement concerning Master de Sales' piety spoken by the fun-loving lads. All reverenced the devout practices.

In addition to the regular course of studies, Francis now learned fencing, dancing and riding, accomplishments deemed so necessary to produce a polished gentleman. Master de Sales, being an unusually graceful and dexterous lad, was the pride and joy of his teachers, and the envy and torture of his less-talented comrades who were often admonished to "observe the young lord from the Chablais."

"You should see how Francis fences," Gaspard excitedly told his father who was visiting the boys at college.

"The way he handles his horse, now that is something," sighed Louis.

"But, he excels in dancing! He's ever so much better than Monsieur Coté," added the third cousin.

"In other words," laughingly remarked Francis' uncle, "you have not only a paragon of virtue, but a masculine Diana and Terpsichore and Past-master of Fencing all combined in one single individual whom you boys are fortunate enough to call cousin."

On an autumnal holiday, when the leaves were beginning to turn tobacco brown and holly-berry red Francis and his group of friends set out in the company of M. Deage for a three league hike to the little town of Isles in the river Fier. Wild purple foxgloves with their bell-like blooms pointed their shaking fingers at the carefree boys. Monsieur Deage, glancing at the roadside covered with these flowers, called the attention of the group to the healing properties of the blossoms.

"Someday science will find great uses for the digitalis," he prophesized, "already some doctors are trying to prove to the skeptical that it cures diseases of the heart."

"Why do they call the foxglove, digitalis?" questioned Gaspard, the budding naturalist of the crowd.

"I suppose, because one can fit his fingers into the blossoms so easily and exactly," answered the tutor.

The somnalence of noon lay on the tiny village of Isles, and the miniature inland lake drowsed in the mild October sun as the boys, laughing and teasing, prepared to satisfy their keen and healthy appetites as they rested, relaxed, on the banks of the placid lake.

"Let us, first of all say a prayer to God," suggested Francis. "Let us thank Him for making those blessed shade trees, that sweet, newly-mown meadow, and this peaceful, quiet little lake."

While food and drink relieved the imperative demands of hunger, intimate and delightful tales of work and of play, about pupils and teachers, were spun from fact and fancy by the merry children. All too soon it was time to return to Annecy. Though the foot-sore little caravan entered the college town in the midst of a soft blur of rain, their exuberant spirits were not dampened until Monsieur Deage announced in solemn tones, "The fun is now over, young gentlemen. To serious study now."

December the 17th was a red-letter day for Francis. In the bitter chill of that morning he had the supreme happiness of making his First Holy Communion, and of receiving the Sacrament of Confirmation at the hands of Bishop Ange Justiniani. The quaint little Dominican church was crowded with parents and friends of the children who were to receive the two sacraments. Fair doublets, slashed hose, richly-chased rapiers and costly cloaks, heavy with gold and silver embroidery, sparkling coifs and jeweled stomachers and glittering veils proclaimed the rank and wealth of those kneeling in the front rows, while gaily attired peasants, in full skirts and tight bodices, or full baggy trousers, prayed with fervor and smiled with satisfaction at the lovely, heart-warming scene of innocent girls and boys receiving their Lord for the first time, and being knighted soldiers of Jesus Christ, by the regally attired Bishop of Geneva.

From the time of his first Holy Communion, Francis, who had given serious and prayerful thought to the idea, resolved to become a priest.

The Where, When and How were slowly approaching.

From busy lip to busy lip passed the word that Monsignor Gallois Regard, Bishop of Bogneray, in the absence of Bishop Justiniani, was about to hold an ordination at Clermont. Francis, after earnest prayer, asked his father's permission to receive the tonsure. Knowing that the ceremony did not bind the recipient to become a religious, and depending upon Parisian influences to change his son's predilection, the Lord of Boisy consented.

According to the custom of the times, Francis did not don the clerical dress, but continued to wear the sword and costume of a young nobleman. Though a mere lad of twelve, he formulated certain rules of conduct: prayers, spiritual reading, visits to the Blessed Sacrament and frequent Communion became part and parcel of his schedule. During his last years at Annecy his good nature and self control were often sorely tried, not only by his mischievous companions, but also by M. Deage who attempted to wean the youth from too much 'bookish learning.' Francis, quick-tempered and keenly sensitive, carefully hid his natural feelings and displayed amidst the fiercest temptations a calm and serene countenance. This control acquired only by sheer dint of prayer and self-discipline was to benefit Francis all his life.

* * *

Paris, cradle of famous cathedrals, noble universities, fresh thoughts and new fashions! What heart would not thrill at the very mention of a long sojourn in the fascinating city on the Seine where rich past and richer present dwell side by side!

When Monsieur de Boisy proposed that, the lessons at Annecy college being completed, his son should study in the French capital there was only one fly in Francis' ointment. The college of Navarre, selected by Monsieur as the one most frequented by the young nobility of Europe and particularly of Savoy, did not merit Francis' approval. Feeling more and more drawn to the ecclesiastical state, he was fearful lest the worldly atmosphere of this fashionable College might draw him from his high ideals as he was still at the impressionable stage of life. Somehow, he must cautiously represent his disapproval to his father.

The occasion presented itself sooner than Francis had dared hope. On a frosty morning as the newly-laid fire cheerfully blazed and crackled in the music room where Gasparde de Sales was painstakingly practicing "Chansons de Roland" Francis noticed that his mother's usual tranquillity was marred. Without asking the cause of her annoyance, he gently folded his arms around her and whispered, "Let us ask God about it, dear mother; He will help us, He will aid us."

"That is well-spoken, my dear boy," said his mother, returning his caress. "But I notice that you, too, seem disturbed, perplexed . . pre-occupied — I know not what it is."

"Mother," responded Francis, rejoicing at the opportunity to disclose his fears, "Let us take a little walk under the chestnut trees. Wrap up well as it's quite chilly."

Mother and son, in one of those sweet intimacies that exist only between kindred souls, discussed the problem thoroughly as they walked up and down.

"You see, mother," explained Francis, "I am most eager to go to Paris to secure the religious and secular training that will prove so beneficial in later years. You know the deepest desire of my heart is to become a priest. I feel, however, that Navarre College will prove a hindrance rather than a help."

"Have you any school in mind, my dear boy?"

"Yes, mother. The Jesuit College at Clermont," was the immediate answer.

"The good Jesuits have an enviable reputation for learning and wisdom. I believe I can convince your father of the prudence of your choice."

The outcome of Madame de Boisy's interview with her husband was that he, after carefully weighing the pro's and con's, generously decided to allow Francis to enroll at the Jesuit House of Studies.

In Clermont, the good Fathers, charmed with Francis' courtly manners and noble virtues, welcomed him with great courtesy and arranged for him to follow their classes as an extern. Lodgings were procured for him and his two attendants at Hotel de la Rose Blanche, opposite the college and for the next decade of years, French, Latin, Greek, Hebrew, theology, philosophy and many other branches of learning occupied most of Francis' days and parts of his nights. At the College of Clermont he was known as Monsieur de Villaroget, a title bestowed upon him from one of his father's estates.

Sundays, holydays and holidays found the student visiting the historic church of Notre Dame where the delicately-pointed arches and flawless stained glass windows not only raised his heart in prayer, but recalled poignant scenes of splendid pageantry and royal coronations, which he had read about in both sacred and profane history. Montmartre, the Hill of Martyrs, where St. Denis, the first Bishop of Paris, met his death, and the quaint suburb of Paris, St. Denis itself, the burial place of the martyred saint and of many, many French kings, were frequently visited and venerated by the young Savoyard.

In 1586 Francis was summoned home by his ambitious father who decided that his son was to take the degree of jurisprudence at the University of Padua. Most determined was Monsieur de Boisy that his heir should receive an education befitting his rank and birth. Moreover, he secretly cherished the fond hope that Francis, having received a degree in law, would become a brilliant senator. Too, there was the matter of a broad, general education— Monsieur de Villaroget had spent some years in France, now he must sojourn in Italy. Since Savoy lay between these two great countries it was necessary that Francis understand the different ambitions and temperaments of these two places and their peoples—conditions which profoundly influenced the life of the little tucked-in Duchy.

Francis was delighted with the idea of studying at Padua, the famed university city under Venetian rule. He had always looked upon this particular university as a center of sacred knowledge, and he could drink freely and deeply, at first hand, those subjects dear and close to his heart. Then there was the added attraction of being able to study under the celebrated professor Guy Pancirola whose fame had spread even to Paris.

Monsieur de Boisy again selected M. Deage to accompany the student and the ever-faithful Georges Rolland was again with the two travelers. After all preparations were completed for a long sojourn in Italy the trio set out towards the southern peninsula. It was winter and crossing the Alps was doubly hazardous, however, the men succeeded in making the difficult passes without mishap, and reached Padua in the early days of February, 1588.

At this time about twenty thousand students followed the various lectures. To each chair two professors, one a native, the other a foreigner, were appointed. About forty monasteries rivalled each other in the cultured pursuit of university degrees. Especially famous were the great Franciscan convent attached to the Church of St. Anthony and the College of the Jesuits.

Francis, the scholar, followed the same life of prayer and study in Padua that he had inaugurated in Paris at the Jesuit College. In addition to attending the lectures he devoted eight hours a day to study, four to law and the remainder to theology. Very seldom was he called upon to deviate from this schedule. At times the intense and concentrated work was irksome, both mind and body rebelled against the constant application. Then it was that the youth encouraged himself, "Courage, Francis. Why have you come here? Some day you will regret a misuse of your present opportunities."

At Clermont Francis had belonged to the Sodality of the Jesuit College, now, at the invitation of the Jesuits in Padua, he joined the confraternity at their college. He did not distinguish himself here by holding office as he did in France, but he gained eminent renown by his exactitude in obeying all the rules and by his faithfulness in attending the meetings. "Thoroughness of execution" was his motto and this he carried out in every detail of his life.

And thus five years passed swiftly and smoothly as he dwelt beneath serene blue skies in the sun-kissed land of Italy. Frequently on his way to and from classes at the University he knelt in the great basilica that sheltered the beloved Paduan, St. Anthony.

By a strange coincidence, Father Antoine Possevin, S. J. whose acquaintance Francis had made in Paris was stationed in Padua. Francis, delighted, entrusted the direction of his soul to this eminent Jesuit. He it was who is said to have predicted that Francis would one day become the Bishop of Geneva.

For the first time in his college life Francis now became an object of ridicule and derision. Sometimes it was his valor that was challenged; at other times it was his virtue.

On a balmy evening in early spring when most young men's fancies "lightly turn to thoughts of love," three of Francis' classmates, determining to test his virtue, told him that a learned professor from the renowned University of Cordova had arrived in Padua and as they were on their way to call upon him, they invited Francis to accompany them. Unsuspectingly, Francis graciously went with them to the address they mentioned. A richly attired, dark-haired senorita, with dreamy black eyes greeted them sweetly as she introduced herself as Sarita Cadiz, daughter of the Spanish professor. She charmingly apologized that her father was busy with other visitors, stating that he would soon free himself and be with the boys. The young woman was in reality a courtesan, selected by the three to test Francis' virtue.

The oldest of the boys was the first to leave the room on the plea of a forgotten message.

After a few minutes Jacques awkwardly retreated saying, "Give my profound respects to your esteemed father, Senorita Sarita. Tell him that I am sorry to miss him, but I am due at a philosophy lecture at nine."

Shortly Phillipe, who was really loathe to leave Francis, made his adieu mumbling, "Ma mere is waiting for me to accompany her to Mademoiselle Virgaude's concert."

Finding herself alone with the polished, debonair Monsieur de Villaroget, the exotic senorita immediately exerted her blandishments. Francis at once realized that an attack on his virtue was in process; he indignantly repelled the woman's advances, addressing her in stern unyielding words. Finding that nothing was able to dismay her, he resorted to abuse.

"What kind of a person are you to force yourself upon a man (he was twenty-one at the time) who not only despises all that you and your kind stands for, but finds no attraction whatsoever in you? Away from me!" Then emphasizing his utter distaste, he calmly spit at her.

This was indeed too much for the passionate Spanish Miss who sat back and poured forth a torrent of foul abuse at her would-be captive. Francis, taking advantage of her lengthy disparagement, was able to free himself from her and quit the odious place. Not only did he when he next met the culprits, tell them that he saw through their evil designs, but he spoke so earnestly and kindly to them they were overwhelmed with remorse and played no further pranks.

It was during Holy Week that another incident occurred that tested the young man's valor. Francis, returning from Tenebrae services at the Mother House of the Reformed Benedictines, was softly humming the "Stabat Mater" when he was waylaid and set upon by a group of ruffians. These men, really college boys, had no intention of actually harming their victim, they merely planned to frighten and cow him so that they might boast of his cowardice and of their bravery. When Francis, at the first sign of danger whipped his sword from its scabbard his would-be assailants were nonplussed. His skillful handling of the weapon astonished and bewildered them. Here was not only an excellent student but a master swordsman!

Without wasting a moment they quickly and abjectly apologized and thereafter were loud in their praises of the skill and prowess of the surprising Monsieur de Villaroget.

As soon as the full course of his studies was completed Francis, according to the wishes of his father, presented his application to the University to take his degree of Doctor of Law. Francis was twenty-four years old. It was necessary for him to take an oral examination which would be public. Pancirola, his teacher and promoter, wishing to give the occasion as much solemnity as possible assembled forty-eight doctors to examine the candidate. The gathering was presided over by the Bishop of Padua. The examinee answered all questions put to him and passed with outstanding success. Then ensued an exchange of congratulatory speeches.

Pancirola, turning to Francis spoke, "I hold myself fortunate in being able to preside at today's ceremony. I have been looking forward to this occasion when I should see you receive the doctorate as one of the happiest days of my life. One cannot love virtue without loving you. Your noble virtue is on a level with the knowledge which you have shown, and by the qualities of your heart, which rival in purity the brilliance of your mind. You have kept yourself pure in the midst of a licentious town, like the fountain of Arethusa which in mingling its waters with the sea, loses not its sweetness. In fact, the sincere horror of all that is evil, the constant practice of all that is good, are joined in you in the most admirable manner, and with the most genuine piety: these are the virtues which heaven rewards by the honors you are receiving today."

Upon the conclusion of Pancirola's congratulations, Francis addressed the assembly, "Although I fully realize that it behooves me to offer you my deepest thanks for the signal favor you have conferred upon me today I feel that I am unequal to express my gratitude in a manner befitting the occasion. When I decided to apply myself to the sacred science of law I needed little counsel to determine where I should learn it. This University of Padua drew me at once by the greatness of its renown as it possesses doctors and professors who are as like to be without rival in the future as they have been without equal in the past. Since I have not the eloquence to express my thanks, and you have not the leisure for a longer discourse, I beg you to accept this protestation which I now voice in the presence of this noble assembly. I here acknowledge and declare that whatever worth I may claim to have, I owe it entirely, most noble friends, to this most illustrious college of doctors."

Bowing to Pancirola with deepest respect, Francis continued, "And now it remains for me to beg you, my dear Pancirola, my most renowned master, to bestow upon me with your kindly hands the insignia which the University is accustomed to grant to those whom she has made her alumni."

At this request, Pancirola bestowed the ring and privileges of the university upon the graduate. Crowning Francis' fair head with the traditional wreathe and doctor's cap, he exclaimed: "The University is happy to find in you all those qualities of mind and heart which it can desire. All this happiness is made complete by the fact that the testimony of esteem which it gives you, in admitting you to the number of doctors, has the unstinted and unanimous approval of all those who are judges of real merit."

* * *

After a leisurely and delightful trip through the Eternal City where all places of religious and classical fame were visited, Francis and his two companions proceeded to Loretto, passing through Spolito, the scene of Hannibal's ignoble defeat, and Malerata, fragrant with the golden mimosa blossoms. The last stop on their itinerary before leaving the land of poets, students and lovers was Venice, the glowing bride of the Adriatic. Here the three spent several sunny days and moon-lit nights visiting the famous churches and places of interest, and riding in the picturesque gondolas enchanted with the gaily-clad gondoliers singing their plaintive love songs as they sculled their oars in the shinning blue waters.

After a final visit to St. Marks where Francis thanked the Mother of God for her gracious care and assistance during his years in the southern land, the newly-made doctor addressed his friends, "Come, I have thanked her to whom I owe the most. Now, let us set out westward towards our beloved Savoy."

CHAPTER III

ROSY DRIFTS OF CHESTNUT BLOSSOMS

IN the cool, clean air of an early May morning, when rosy drifts of chestnut blossoms fell lightly on a little cavalcade of three who had reined in their horses as they approached the long, winding driveway that led to Chateau de la Thuile, a shout of joy pierced the clear air. It startled the quiet horses whose riders were gazing in contentment at the enchanting springtime scene, the picturesque chateau surrounded by fragrant fruit trees which were laden with clouds of blooms. Bernard who had been commissioned to be on the alert for his returning brother and his escorts, after one hearty shout, was scampering off to rouse the de Boisy household.

Before Francis and his two friends could dismount, Madame and Monsieur with their four sons and daughter hastened to greet the new arrivals.

"One moment," kindly remarked Monsieur de Boisy, as he noticed the confusion and realized the impossibility of their all welcoming the return ing student at one and the same time. Courteously turning to M. Deage, he and his two older sons managed to give the others time to dismount before they were engulfed in the floods of welcome.

"My son," murmured the lovely chatelaine of La Thuile, as she warmly embraced her first-born, "How I have missed you these many years. Still, why should I say that? You have always been in my heart and in my prayers."

"Mother dear," replied her devoted son, "memories of you have perfumed my waking and sleeping hours. Long ago you told us what to do and what to avoid. You repeated to me the words Queen Blanche spoke to her son, Louis, telling me they were your sentiments, also. The thought of you, my mother, has always brought a song to my heart and a smile to my lips."

"Come dear, greet your brothers and sister," chided the fond mother, too filled with happiness for further words.

It was with some difficulty that Francis recognized the tall, fair, striking lads he had teasingly parted from five years previously. It was also, with a certain amount of amusement that he managed to engage Bernard in conversation with him; the lad was standing to one side with Monsieur Rolland, and casting shy, timid glances at this big brother.

Monsieur de Boisy, enchanted with his courtly-mannered son, turned to the group saying, "Come, let us have some refreshments and continue our conversation in the dining hall."

Lightly resting her fingers on her tall son's arm, Madame de Boisy and Francis led the way into the spacious, old chateau.

It was just before bed-time when little Bernard's head was beginning to nod that Francis remembered the gifts he had so carefully purchased for his loved ones. "Ladies first," he smilingly remarked as he presented packages to his mother and Gasparde.

"Francis," exclaimed his delighted sister as she quickly opened hers, "you are dear to remember my fondness for bon-bons and cherries glâce."

"My thoughtful son," said his mother as she carefully displayed a beautifully equipped sewing box, inlaid with precious wood and mother-of-pearl. What exquisite taste. I shall always cherish this gift."

Francis, making a low bow before his youngest brother who was now wide awake, handed him a small, oblong package.

"What is it Francis?" demanded the excited lad, as he gazed at the pretty box with its pictured cover.

"Here, let me wind it up for you. Now, listen carefully."

Sweet strains of Celano's heavenly "Tantum Ergo" filled the hall. This hymn was followed by Charles d'Orleans' charming rondeau, "Le temps a laisie son manteau."

"The year has changed his mantle cold
Of wind, of rain, of bitter air;
And he goes clad in cloth of gold,
Of laughing suns and seasons fair;
No bird or beast of wood or wold
But doth with cry or song declare
The year lays down his mantle cold.
All fount, all rivers, seaward rolled,
The pleasant summer livery wear,
With silver studs on broidered vair;
The world puts off its rainment old
The year lays down his mantle cold."

The de Boisys listened enraptured until the last strains had died away. For a few moments no one spoke. Then Monsieur de Boisy's voice broke the sweet silence.

"Where did you ever buy this," he asked as he gently fingered the music box.

"In a little out-of-the-way Italian book shop. How this little instrument happened to be there is a mystery. Still, you know what odd assortments one often comes across in such places .. To tell the truth," continued Francis, "I was selecting this book for you, when I chanced upon the box. I myself was so fascinated that I couldn't resist getting it for Bernard."

The book Francis gave his father was "Spiritual Combat," one the delighted lord found to be of utmost comfort for the rest of his life. Books, too, beautiful and rich with exquisite illumination, were given to the three older boys who were at the age to appreciate good literature.

When all the presents had been duly re-examined and exclaimed over, nothing would do until Bernard could play, once again, his lovely music box. Later that night upon retiring, after family prayers had been said and a special one of gratitude added for the safe return of the young lord, Francis found himself humming the words of the Latin hymn while in her room Gasparde softly sang the French lyric.

After days of lavish hospitality, when the doors of la Thuile were flung open wider than usual to welcome all who called to meet the returned son and to congratulate his esteemed parents, Monsieur de Boisy called his son aside and spoke to him about his future.

"Francis, your mother and I, after considering

everything, judge it wise that you should go to Chambery, and be admitted as an advocate by the Senate of Savoy."

Obeying his father's wishes, and again accompanied by Abbe Deage, Francis set out for Chambery where in the course of a solemn session he was unanimously received by the Senate. It was on the newly-made advocate's return from Chambery that an incident occurred that made a most lasting impression on him and Abbe Deage.

The horse on which Francis was riding suddenly stumbled and threw the rider to the ground. As the young man fell, his sword slipped from its scabbard and the scabbard from the baldrick; sword and scabbard formed a complete cross on the path. This incident was repeated not once but twice. Abbe Deage who knew Francis was an expert rider and never had difficulty in retaining his seat, regarded the falls and thrice-formed cross as portents. The Lord must be manifesting Himself to Francis as surely as He had to Saul on the road to Damascus. The young lord must not only put aside his worldly dress, but he must don the priestly cassock and enlist under Christ's standard and devote himself to the salvation of souls.

* * *

Monsieur de Boisy, ever eager for his son's ad-

vancement, was delighted to learn of his success at
Chambery. Plan after plan unfolded in his mind
as he thought over future triumphs for the young
heir who would prove a source of pride and comfort for his declining years . . . . An honorable
marriage (he selected a pleasing young lady whom
he deemed a fit consort for his accomplished son)
. . . . a lucrative position (Francis must become
president of the Senate in a few years) . . . . the
estate of Villargot (some improvements must be
made immediately at the chateau) . . . . all kinds of

> "Day dreams, night dreams,
> Play dreams, pipe dreams"

flitted and nested in the Lord of Boisy's active
mind.

Francis, however, had other plans. How was
he to dispel his fond father's dreams without mortally wounding him? Again, he took his mother
into his confidence, and sought the help of his
cousin, Louis de Sales, who had been his college
campanion at Annecy. Francis' mother at first
opposed his plans, but having satisfied herself that
his vocation was from God, she not only approved
of his ambition but promised to aid him in every
possible way and began, secretly, to make a cassock.

Louis, now a Canon of the Cathedral, was delighted at the idea of his cousin's desire, but urged

him not to hasten matters feeling that God, in His own good time, would bring events to a happy issue.

It so happened that in October of the year 1592, the Provost of the Chapter of Geneva, Francis Empereur, died. Louis de Sales now saw a way which might make Monsieur de Boisy consent to Francis' priestly vocation. First, Louis approached the Bishop of Geneva, Claude de Granier, who had met and admired the young advocate, Francis. With the Bishop's hearty approval, Canon Louis then entreated for Francis, from Rome, the position of Provost of the Chapter. In due time the papal bulls were dispatched from Rome to Annecy where they arrived the following May. In those days Louis merely followed the ordinary procedure to fill a vacancy of this type.

Francis was overcome with surprise when his cousin showed him the bulls of appointment. He realized, however, that if anything was to be done about his vocation now was the time to seize "time by the forelock" and speak to his father.

"Father," he said, as he and Louis entered the garden fragrant with choice blooms and sweet with the song of birds. "I have come to ask you a great favor; if you can see your way to granting it, I will never ask you for anything else."

"Tell me what it is you want," suggested Monsieur de Boisy, thinking it was doubtless something about a marriage settlement.

"That you will grant me your permission, father, to become a priest. Here are the apostolic bulls by which Clement VIII confers upon me the provostship of the church of St. Peter in Geneva, the highest dignity, as you know in the diocese next to that of Bishop."

Totally unprepared for such an emergency, Francis' father was speechless for a time. All of his ambitious plans for this brilliant son were felled with one cruel blow! Gradually recovering his usual composure and eloquence he protested, "My boy, take care what you are doing. You are made for greater things than this. You have spent many years in studying. Are all your labors to be wasted? Who has put this idle, foolish notion into your head? Do not act hastily, I beg of you."

"Father," explained Francis patiently, "from my earliest youth, nay, even from my boyhood, I have felt a strong inclination for the priesthood. I feel that God has truly inspired me to devote myself to His most holy service. I had that intention when I received the tonsure; my visit to the Holy House of Loretto enkindled still further the desire. Recently, God has signified His Will to me by a most extraordinary sign." He then proceeded to relate the incident attending his return from Chambery.

Then, flinging himself at his father's feet, he entreated with tear-filled eyes, "Father, I beg you to grant me this favor, beyond which I have no desire. Give me your blessing in the name of God."

Monsieur de Boisy, every inch a hero, now generously and bravely yielded to his son's entreaties· "My son, do what the Lord demands of you. Who am I to resist? May God ever bless you and in His name I grant you my paternal blessing."

On the feast of the Ascension Francis was temporarily installed as the new Provost. Since only doctors and nobles were admitted to this dignity (Francis de Sales was both) Monsieur de Boisy was reconciled and even pleased when his son resigned his title and the estate of Villaroget, and under the guidance of Abbe Bouvard, began his retreat in preparation for Minor Orders.

On the Ember Saturday before the Feast of the Holy Trinity, Francis was ordained sub-deacon in the church of St. Francis at Annecy. In order to celebrate the auspicious occasion, the Bishop of Geneva invited the newly-made sub-deacon and his family to dinner.

Francis, ever-witty, remarked during the course of the dinner with his naive charm, "My lord, evidently you liken me to the prodigal son, since you are giving this banquet of rejoicing to commemorate my entry into your sacerdotal family."

Claude de Granier answered, "Now in truth, you are my son and my sub-deacon, upon whom God is abundantly lavishing His graces. Until yesterday, however, you had received nothing from me. Bishop Justiniani, my predecessor, confirmed you, and Monsignor de Bagneray gave you the tonsure. Soon I shall do more for you."

Time sped quickly and profitably for the young Levite who from June to December was busily engaged in giving sermons, visiting the sick, reciting the Office, exhorting those who were lax in their religious duties, and in acting as peacemaker among those who quarreled. Francis' powers as an orator soon began to attract attention. The delighted audiences marveled at the eloquence and learning of the young preacher. Fullness and beauty flowed from his lips like honey from the honeycomb. His sermons were not too long, nor too severe. The practice of virtue was made attractive to all, and charity was emphasized as the cream of all virtues.

"An act in itself altogether trivial, might be performed with much grace and charity, while a very brilliant and dazzling work might be animated by a very feeble spark of love of God. Intensity of love, that is the only rule by which to ascertain the value of one's actions," urged the love-inspired Provost.

It was during these months that an interchange of letters began between Antoine Favre, Senator and one of the most brilliant men in Savoy, and Francis. This correspondence was to initiate and cement a friendship, deep and sweet, which would be broken only by death.

Too, during these days the young apostle organized the Confraternity of the Cross to help combat the spiritual and temporal evils that were undermining the faith and solidarity of some Catholics in the heresy-infected regions about Geneva. When all rules and regulations were drawn up, Francis submitted the whole to the Bishop who gave his warmest approval to the project. The Duke of Savoy was so pleased with the Confraternity that he granted it the privilege of releasing each year, on Holy Thursday, a criminal condemned to death or to the galleys.

Claude de Granier, noticing Francis' glowing zeal and successful labors, decided that the young nobleman should be raised to the priesthood as soon as possible so that the scope of his office should be as wide as possible. Accordingly, Francis was told to prepare for his ordination which would be held in the Ember week of Advent.

As the day for his ordination drew near Francis was seized with anxiety. Thoughts of the wonderful powers about to be conferred upon him overwhelmed him. He voiced these sentiments in a letter to Antoine Favre when he informed him of the greatness of the honor which was soon to be conferred, "Nothing so arduous and so perilous can ever happen to mortal man as to hold in his hands, and in the words of St. Jerome produce by his words That which the angels themselves cannot worthily celebrate. I am not ignorant of this sublime dignity. It is an event which changes one's whole life. We humans can never, my dear Antoine, thank God sufficiently for such dignities as He confers."

With such sentiments Francis was ordained on the early morning of December 15th and on the 21st he celebrated with a heart overpowered with love, his first Holy Mass in the Cathedral of Annecy which was packed with his devoted family, relatives and friends. Shortly before the New Year he was officially installed as Provost of the Chapter of the Cathedral Church of Annecy.

Chapter IV

FRAGRANT, FULL-BLOWN RED ROSES

THE cathedral church at Annecy was thronged, partly with Calvinists who were curious to hear the newly-ordained Provost, partly with Catholics who were eager to hear once again the eloquent words of Father Francis. In the glowing words that fell like scintillating jewels the Catholics found firmer conviction in their faith and the Calvinists discovered their deep-seated beliefs strangely shaken. In all that vast assembly there was one person who was not slow in voicing his strong disapproval of the sermon.

"My son," chided Monsieur de Boisy,"in former times the sermons were learned, well-thought-out, full of wonderful things. There was more Latin and Greek quoted in one of those talks than there is in ten of yours. Everyone was delighted, edified. As to your sermons, why your language is too simple, even a child would understand it. That is not the way great men should discourse."

Francis, smiling, took it all in good part. He realized that his father was speaking in all frankness according to his lights, and the maxims of the world. Since however, the maxims of the gospel, were Francis' guide, he continued to model his talks on those of the Divine Preacher, Jesus Christ.

Another heartache was soon to be endured by poor Monsieur de Boisy. It so happened that Charles Emmanuel, son of Emmanuel Philibert of Savoy, having reconquered the Duchy of Chablais and the bailiwicks of Gex, Ternier and Gaillard from Henry IV of France, petitioned the Bishop of Geneva to select a certain number of ecclesiastics of edifying life and to send them as missionaries into the newly-conquered provinces which had become largely Calvinistic. Claude de Granier immediately held a meeting of the priests of his diocese to consult them on the best method of carrying out the Duke's wishes. The prospect the Bishop presented was most discouraging — for over sixty years the Catholic religion had been uprooted with all the sacrilegious and fanatic fury that marked the Reformation everywhere. Lovely old churches had been desecrated, sacred crosses had been trampled on, costly statues had been destroyed and flourishing monasteries had been demolished. Having clearly stated the facts and presented the difficulties of the hazardous undertaking his lordship concluded by asking for volunteers.

For a short time no one spoke. The embryonic project seemed already to bear the earmarks of failure. Then the young Provost, his soul aflame with courage at the dismal proposal from which all others shrank, rose to his feet and turning to his Bishop spoke, "My lord, if you think me capable of this mission, and if you order me to undertake it, I am ready to obey and shall hold myself happy in your choice. 'In thy word I will let down the net.' I ask for no assistants at present, only my cousin Louis."

The Bishop's fatherly face lighted with approval as he smiled at Francis. "Not only do I think you eminently suited for this office," he replied, "but I feel that it is particularly fitting that you become a leader in this apostolic work. Had you not offered, in spite of my ill-health, I myself should have felt obliged to have undertaken the mission."

Monsieur de Boisy was not long in learning of the new turn of events. At once, without a word to anyone, the heart-broken old warrior mounted his horse and rode off to Annecy. Here he made his way to his son's house where he voiced his disapproval in well-chosen words.

Francis, deeply moved by this example of paternal affection, remained obdurate, answering each objection with the crusader's slogan, "Deus vult, God wills it, dear father."

Finally the testy nobleman, seeing that he was making no headway with his son exclaimed, "Very well then, come with me to the Bishop. He will not resist the tears of a father."

Scarcely were they admitted into the Bishop's residence before Monsieur de Boisy fell on his knees before Msgr. de Granier. "My lord," he pleaded, "I permitted my son to devote himself to the church as a Confessor, but never will I consent that he should become a Martyr and that you should send him to the butchery, like a victim to be torn to pieces by those Calvinist wolves."

The Bishop, forcibly moved, was ready to yield to the tearful entreaties, had not Francis exclaimed, "My lord, hold firm! I have put my hand to the plow. Do you want me to look back for human considerations?"

Glancing from father to son, Claude de Granier spoke, "Remember you both bear the name of the illustrious Francis of Assisi. Beware, Monsieur de Boisy, lest resistance should lead your son to imitate this patron and cast off his very clothes as did the Seraphic Saint, and thus stripped of all things, follow the standard of the Crucified."

Monsieur de Boisy, determining to move heaven and earth if necessary, would not surrender.

* * *

Notwithstanding his father's opposition, Francis, accompanied only by his cousin Louis, set out on foot from Annecy on one of those mellow September days when the surrounding country-side was rich with the promise of abundant harvests, and redolent with the fragrance of full-blown red roses. Upon arriving at Allinges, fortress on the frontier of the Chablais, the foot-sore, dust-covered missionaries were kindly greeted by the Captain, Baron d'Harmonce, an old friend of the House of Sales. The baron was delighted to learn of the proposed restoration of Catholicism in the Chablais, ordered a meal to be prepared for the guests and then, recognizing evident signs of fatigue, conducted the two men to the sleeping quarters which had been prepared for them.

The next morning after they had celebrated Mass they breakfasted with the baron. He was a man of great prudence and cautioned them to proceed warily in their work. "Adopt the Fabian policy I am always suggesting to my soldiers," he advised, "and by all means come back to this fortress each night. Among the thirty-one thousand people in these districts there are only one hundred Catholics. Do not attempt to celebrate Mass among them for some time."

Armed with letters to the Magistrates of the town the priests set out on their trip. At Thonon they found only seven families of "the old faith" whose fear of persecution prevented their openly professing and practicing their religion. Francis, after meeting them, urged the little band not to be ashamed of their faith. "I have come to be your pastor," he said, "hereafter we shall meet at stated times at the church of St. Hippolytus."

The little sprinkling of Catholics promised to attend the services and Francis, encouraged by the first day's labor, left Thonon.

At first complete indifference marked the attitude of the Protestant inhabitants but before long violent opposition to the missionaries was aroused by the Huguenots. The God-loving Provost and his cousin were represented as disturbers of the public peace, false prophets, sorcerers. These remarks had the intended effect on their hearers; even the more kindly disposed Protestants carefully avoided the two priests.

The calumnies did not cool Francis' apostolic zeal. On the contrary they fired his enthusiasm. "Now is the time, dear cousin," he remarked to Louis, "to keep up our courage. 'He that dwelleth in the help of the Most High shall abide under the protection of the God of Heaven.' Let us persevere in the hope that God's grace will eventually fructify the seeds we are sowing. Are you willing to continue the struggle?"

"I have not the slightest feeling of fear, Francis. Rather I rejoice to have some little share of the treatment accorded Our Master who bore all false accusations in noble silence. The disciple must be worthy of his Master", answered Louis.

"Very well, then, we are as strong as needs be, and I am determined to carry on this great work. We shall leave no stone unturned in gaining souls. Let us remember, Louis, that above all things we must be kind and gentle in our dealings with these poor, misguided people. More flies are caught with a spoonful of honey than with a barrel of vinegar", concluded the wise Provost.

Francis, fully aware of the hostile attitude of the inhabitants, and realizing that he would at times have to carry the Blessed Sacrament to sick people, devised a method of carrying the Sacred Species in a silver box which he bore upon his breast. Wrapping himself in a long cloak he concealed the pyx so that the average passerby was unaware of the Host. (This method originated by Francis is used today in carrying the Blessed Sacrament in

non-Catholic countries.) Since it was a poignant
grief to Francis that he was obligated to hide the
King of Kings and Lord of Lords from the eyes
of others, and to seemingly deprive Him of honor
due, he tried to atone for this deprivation by
whispering little acts of love and adoration, and
requested Catholics when they might see him
walking with his cloak wrapped closely about him,
to show external reverence and recollection, and
to follow him at a discreet distance.

＊　＊　＊

All too soon the chill winds from the mountain
peaks swept down into the Chablais. In the train
of the winds came heavy rains, intense cold, soft
flurries of snow and brittle hail. It became
dangerous and almost impossible to travel over the
roads and highways of the little towns. Dauntless
in the face of this added opposition, Francis
fastened spikes to his boots and when this pre-
caution failed he would crawl on his hands and
knees over dangerous stretches. Since a severe
form of chilblains had afflicted his hands and feet,
his path was frequently marked by drops of blood
flowing down from his open wounds. What
exquisite torture this indefatigible disciple endured
for his beloved Master!

During these trying days, Monsieur de Boisy was not the only one experiencing severe anxiety in regard to Francis' labors in the hostile Chablais. Antoine Favre had been obliged to go to the valley of Aulps on business, and as he was near Thonon, and deeply concerned in his friend's welfare, he arranged for an interview with Francis. Re-assured by this visit and by chance remarks he picked up in the villages, Monsieur Favre departed from Francis with a lighter heart and frequently wrote enthusiastic and affectionate letters to his dearest friend. What encouragement Francis drew from this noble friendship and exchange of letters he himself stated, "No other thought gives me such pleasant recreation as that by which I daily strive to picture you to myself as vividly as possible. Then, in the midst of deepest darkness a light shines upon me, and oh, dear friend, how dark indeed, is the atmosphere here, ruled by the prince of darkness! Since your departure he has not ceased to darken more and more the minds of the people. The demon perceived at once that the Governor, with several other Catholics, has attempted to promote the affairs of our religion with judgment and prudence. He, infuriated, inspired the chief men of Thonon to call a council and there take an oath that neither they themselves, nor the rest of the people should ever attend any of the Catholic sermons. This took place, I hear, in the town hall.

What can be done, dearest friend? Their hearts are hardened! I think I see the object these miserable men have in view. Doubtless, by depriving us of all hope of effecting anything definite, they wish to force us to take our departure. We, however, on our part have no such intention. Do, dear Antoine, remember us in your prayers."

One evening when night descended more swiftly and bitterly than usual in the Chablais the cousins found themselves in a village where all the doors were securely fastened against the rough onslaughts of the incipient Alpine storm. Like Joseph and his sweet Mary the two men sought shelter from house to house. Cold hostility and curt refusal, even more cutting than the chilling cold, greeted each request for a night's lodging. Finally, in order to protect themselves from the full blasts of the breaking storm, Francis and Louis took refuge in the still-warm oven of the village bakery.

Another time Francis was alone when night overtook him. As he tried to make his way out of the dense woods he heard the angry howls of hungry wolves who, having smelled food, were intent on tracking down their prey. Only one alternative was open! He must evade his ravenous pursuers. He rapidly climbed into a nearby snow-laden hemlock and securely fastened himself to one of the branches with his wide sash. Deep snow lay on the ground, frosty stars with their cold cuttings of light pierced the cloudless skies and a North wind, heavy with the promise of more snow, reminded Francis that only a miracle of God's love could preserve him through the night. Bleak, gray morning found the Provost surrounded by a group of peasants from a neighboring village who had gone early into the forest and discovered the priest in a state of extreme exhaustion. Overcome by the sight of such dauntless courage, and won by the sufferer's uncomplaining manner, they carried him to their home where they carefully nourished the feeble spark of life and vied with one another in little attentions to their gentle guest.

Eventually, the Protestant ministers, particularly infuriated that Francis and his cousin still persisted in their efforts of evangelizing, hired assassins. These would-be-murderers tried time after time to attack the priests; never were they in the least successful.

When news of these threatened attacks reached the ears of Monsieur de Boisy he became more distressed than ever and ordered Francis, through a special messenger, to return to Annecy at once. Francis' reply to his father was so noble, courageous and respectful that once and for all Monsieur de Boisy ceased struggling his son's activities and openly aided and encouraged him.

About this time Antoine Favre who had been writing a treatise on "Conjectures on Civil Laws" dedicated the twelfth volume to Francis. In his dedication he wrote:

"Since your kindness has admitted me into the inner sanctuary of your friendship, I have seen how much you deserve to be loved even by those who are not bound to you by any tie. And who would have so little sense as not to admire, love and honor the noble qualities by which you have acquired such renown? . . I do not speak of your learning, eloquence, the fruits of a fertile and cultivated mind. There is in you something far more preferable—your goodness, your moderation, your unfailing calmness of temper, and all those other virtues of a truly noble soul. For myself, I shall feel that I have gained everything, if my book passes down to posterity as a little monument of our close union, in order to make known to all that never has anyone loved you more nor placed greater value on your friendship than I."

* * *

At the beginning of Lent Francis decided to make Thonon his headquarters. Madame du Foug, widow of the former Procurator-General of the Chablais, and a distant relative of the House of Sales, was most happy to extend to him the hospitality of her home, and called her guest by the loving title of son.

Daily Mass was now celebrated in the nearby chapel of St. Stephen, in Marin and the handful of Catholics were happy in the feeling that now indeed they had the good shepherd in the midst of the little flock.

With joyful enthusiasm Francis undertook, in addition to his Lenten duties at Thonon, the task of giving a series of conferences to the soldiers quartered at Allinges. The results of these talks far exceeded his expectations. Having seen the glories of battle contrasted with the glories of holiness, and hearing in soul-stirring words the grand truths of the Incarnation and Redemption the soldiers were so impressed and converted that the whole atmosphere of the garrison was completely altered.

Few are the hearts that fail to react to kindness! Though the hostile attitude of the Huguenots seemed as unalterable as the laws of the Medes and

Persians, Francis' clemency in his dealings with his enemies, his forgiveness of his would-be assassins, and his little, practical aids in trying to relieve the suffering whom he met all tended slowly but surely to make a faint, but real impression on their flinty hearts. Soon to Francis' intense delight, three outstanding heretics showed an interest in the "old faith." Pierre Poncet, a brilliant lawyer and a man of great virtue, was the first to abjure Calvinism. Pierre Fournier, judge of Thonon, was the next to follow, and on the feast of St. Francis of Assisi, in 1596, a day ever dear to Francis, the Baron d'Avulley, the most distinguished man in Chablais, was converted. The good tidings spread rapidly. The abjuraton of these three notables was cause for great rejoicing and many hesitating Calvinists, moved by the powerful example of these three converts sought to openly embrace the Catholic faith. When the news of the recantation of Baron d'Avulley reached Clement VIII, the pope, overwhelmed with joy, sent a special message of congratulation to Francis and the Duke of Savoy, delighted in the wonderful success, summoned Francis to his court.

Leaving Louis in charge of Chablais, Francis set off for Annecy to consult his Bishop and to ask his suggestions in regard to the approaching interview with Charles Emmanuel. Armed with these proposals, the Provost in company with Georges Rolland, left for Italy.

Despite numerous difficulties and the severity of the November weather, the two travelers were able to cross the Great St. Bernard Pass, and after spending a night in the famous monastery which the Saint of Clairvaux had built on the Alpine height, they cautiously descended the perilous slopes and entered Aosta in safety. The remaining trip from Aosta to Turin was made with comparative ease and comfort.

Early the next morning, Charles Emmanuel convoked the Privy Council and requested Francis to place before them those suggestions which, in his estimation, might further conversions in the Chablais.

"I have already suggested in a letter to your Most Serene Highness, that churches must be rebuilt, parish priests must be appointed and installed, certain fixed revenues must be assigned for this work, and a College of Jesuits must be established in Thonon," responded Francis.

"We bear those proposals in mind," encouragingly answered the Duke.

"I now add," continued Francis, " that there should be at least eight preachers, released and

freed from all other duties, that in the town of
Thonon the Holy Office should be chanted in suitable manner, for this purpose the Cure should have
the assistance of six other priests, and my final idea
is that some form of the old Huguenot consistory
be given to the newly-converted people with this
difference — that the president of the council be a
preacher whom the Bishop will appoint, and that all
corrections be made in the spirit of the gospel."

"Submit your proposals on paper, so that we can
study them at leisure," directed the Duke. "For the
present we authorize you to establish six parish
priests in Chablais and we commission the Papal
Nuncio to see that this matter is carried out and
that the salaries formerly paid to the Calvinist
ministers be given to the priests."

In a few days the Duke announced his decisions
to Francis. Most of the requests were granted. In
addition, a printing press for Catholic books was
to be set up at Annecy, the Canons of the Cathedral Church at Geneva were to regain possession of
the benefice of Armoy, usurped by the Huguenots,
and the Holy Sacrifice was to be celebrated in the
principal church of Thonon.

On Christmas day for the first time in sixty
years, Midnight Mass was celebrated in the church
of St. Hippolytus at Thonon and Francis adminis-

tered Holy Communion to over eight hundred people.

Now that the harvest was indeed ripe, Francis and Louis asked for, and received, the assistance of three Jesuits. Conversions were a matter of daily occurrence. All through the spring and summer months the priests labored with splendid results.

It was early in September, one of the loveliest months in the Chablais, that Forty Hours of Adoration was held at Annemasse with thirty thousand Catholics participating in the glorious event. In the afternoon of the second day of the devotion a beautiful cross was erected on the Geneva road to mark the spot where a former one had been ruthlessly destroyed by the heretics. Catholics and Calvinists read the inscription Francis attached to the tablet:

"It is not the image nor the wood
That the Catholics adore;
But they honor the blood
Of the King who died on the cross."

The Catholics nodded their approval while the startled Huguenots exclaimed, "Our ministers have deceived us. The Catholics do not adore wood and stone, but Jesus Christ."

* * *

Success now marked every effort of the happy

missionaries. No longer were the inhabitants of Thonon and its villages sheep strayed from the true fold. Docile sheep and protecting shepherds dwelt side by side as over the fair, blue waters of Lake Leman, and up and down the fertile valleys of the Chablais, the soft, clear notes of the church bell pealed their inviting call to prayer.

CHAPTER V

CLUMPS OF TALL, STURDY HOLLYHOCKS

A BREATHLESS messenger summoned Francis to Annecy. Claude de Granier was ill and wished to consult the Provost immediately on matters of the utmost importance.

After the bishop had tenderly embraced his favorite priest, and saluted him on both cheeks, in true French fashion, he pleaded, "I must have your help, my son."

"You have only to name your request, my lord," answered Francis.

"I am worn out with fatigue and infirmities and have resolved to name you as my co-adjutor with the succession to the See of Geneva."

Francis alarmed, answered in few words, "My lord, I am thoroughly incapable of such a charge. I am willing to do anything to assist you, but I must refuse the dignity you offer. You do not know me. I have not the necessary humility to save my soul in such an exalted office."

Undismayed by Francis' refusal, the bishop was determined to force him to accept. He realized that the Provost had the necessary qualifications and that only his deep humility prevented his accepting. Having informed the canons of the Chapter of his wish, and receiving their unanimous support the Bishop set out for Sales' castle where he told Madame and Monsieur de Boisy of the choice he had made of their son as his Coadjutor.

Aided by these two powerful allies the Bishop again pleaded with Francis to accept the honor. The young priest remained adamant!

Claude de Granier was not to be defeated in this project dear to his heart. Early one morning as Francis was walking up and down the court-yard of his father's estate he stopped to admire a clump of tall, sturdy hollyhocks which gaily flaunted their vivid, glowing colors.

"Bon jour, mon pere, I am catching the early worm," was the greeting carried on the soft morning breeze.

Turning in the direction of the voice, Francis found Abbe Critain the Bishop's Almoner. "Good morning, Abbe Critain. God be with you. I am admiring these freshly and 'French-ily' garbed blossoms. Very charming, are they not?"

"Indeed, yes," responded the Abbe briefly as he was eager to get down to business. "Our beloved Bishop has sent me to insist that he wishes you to become his Coadjutor. Not only does he order you to accept the position, but he wishes you to know that the clergy, the nobles and all in the diocese wish you to do so."

After a few minutes of deep thought Francis suggested, "Let us go to the church. There we shall each celebrate Mass in honor of The Holy Ghost. During Mass we shall pray for inspiration."

Mass and thanksgiving finished, Francis turned to the patiently waiting Abbe. "Tell his Lordship," he stated gently, "that since he commands, I obey."

Overjoyed, Abbe Critain returned hastily to Annecy where he eagerly informed the determined bishop of the success of his mission.

"God be praised!" exclaimed the venerable prelate with tears of joy in his eyes. "Now that I have obtained Francis de Sales as my coadjutor and successor, I have labored successfully and I have insured things for the welfare of our diocese."

Some months later, Francis, having recovered from a malignant fever which almost carried him off, was on his way to Rome on matters of importance which concerned him as the successor of Claude de Granier. When he reached the Eternal City he found awaiting him his friend, President Favre, who had been sent to Rome on legal matters

by the Duke of Nemours. Together they registered
at the hotel situated near the Church of the Saviour
and then visited St. Peter's to venerate the
tomb of the Apostles. Here Francis earnestly
prayed for the diocese of Geneva and especially for
the people of Chablais. During the following days
the two friends, accompanied by Abbe de Chisse,
the Bishop's Vicar-general, who had gone as a companion with Francis to Rome, visited many famous
shrines and sanctuaries.

In a special audience on March 19th, the Holy
Father received from the hands of Abbe de Chisse
Claude de Granier's petition for Francis de Sales to
be his successor. The following day the Pope summoned Francis into his presence. He greeted the
priest with fatherly affection and told him how
happy the bishop's choice had made him. Before
dismissing his visitor the Pope said. "Hold yourself in readiness to undergo an examinaton in our
presence on Monday, March the 22nd."

Francis, aware of the fact that from time im-
memorial the bishops of Savoy had been exempt
from an examination, was non-plussed. He felt that
were he to submit to the ordeal he would be breaking a precedent, established in favor of his country
for all times. On the other hand, he wished to be
obedient to his Holiness. In his dilemma he sought

the advise of the ambassador of Savoy. The latter at once obtained an audience with Clement VIII and presented the fact that those elected for the episcopacy in Savoy had always been exempt from examinations.

Clement replied, "In this particular instance we have no thought of creating a precedent against such a well-known privilege. We have learned much of the Provost's learning and capabilities and desire an opportunity of enjoying at first hand these talents. Moreover, we desire to display, in the presence of our cardinals, the eminent merit of the bishop-elect."

The ambassador, fully satisfied with Clement's answer, told Francis to prepare himself.

There was little or no time for serious study so lengthy meditations at the foot of the cross, long hours of the night passed in prayer, and the daily offering of the Holy Sacrifice were the only means Francis used as preparation. As he was walking to the pontifical palace on the morning of March 22nd he stopped in the Church of St. James and prayed fervently to God: "O Lord, if Thou knowest that I should be only a useless servant in the episcopal office, and that I have not the requisite zeal for the salvation of souls, permit not that I answer well the questions that will be put to me. Rather, grant that I may be covered with confusion before all and that I may gain nothing from this examination except ignominy."

Utterly abandoned to the Divine Will Francis continued on his way. When he entered the reception room of the palace he saw an immense crowd assembled for the occasion. The Pope was supported by eight cardinals, a score of archbishops, bishops and generals of religious orders, and numbers of protonotaries and canons. A large crowd of lesser visitors filled the hall to overflowing. Clement, Cardinals Borromeo and Borgia and the great Jesuit Bellarmine examined the candidate on difficult and subtle points of theology. Thirty-five points were proposed to him and he answered each with profound wisdom and prudence. All were astonished at the Provost's learning and humility.

At the conclusion of the examination the Pope, thoroughly delighted with Francis' answers, descended from his papal throne and warmly embraced the Savoyard, exclaiming, "Drink, my son, out of thy own cistern, and the stream of thy own well; let thy fountain be conveyed abroad."

The cardinals and other prelates present then pressed forward to add their congratulations to those of the Pope's. Before long the whole city of Rome resounded with the praises of the new bishop, and prince and pauper were eager to make the acquaintance of the distinguished visitor.

Another day in a private audience with Clement, Francis petitioned him to sanction the foundation of the Congregation of the Oratory at Thonon. He had several motives in mind in requesting this foundation. First and foremost, a community of secular clergy living together in the Chablais would educate priests for the thousands of Catholics already gathered into the true fold, and in addition to serving as a seminary it was to be a sort of mechanics' guild. Newly-made converts who now had difficulty in securing work were to be provided with a means of livelihood at the Oratory and lastly, the foundation was to furnish a market for the fruits of their labors. The Pope graciously approved of Francis' plans and in a Bull, Redemptoris et Salvatoris Nostri, designated the house and church of Our Lady of Compassion at Thonon as the house and church of the Oratory. Francis was appointed the first Superior and Cardinal Baronius was named the first Protector of the Oratory of St. Philip Neri at Thonon.

In the lovely month of April, when all nature was preparing to aid in the celebration of the Resurrection by sending forth fresh leaves and delicate spring flowers, Francis and the Vicar-

General returned to Annecy. Francis bore with him his new titles: Coadjutor and Bishop-elect of Geneva, Bishop of Nicopolis and First Superior of the Oratory of Thonon; Abbe de Chisse, the Vicar-General generously and sweetly rejoiced in his companion's honors.

Shortly after Francis' return from Rome there arrived in Savoy an illustrious prelate, Monsignor Vespasian Gribaldi, former Archbishop of Vienna. This Prince of the church had been delegated by the Holy See to make an investigation of the state of religion in the converted territory of the Chablais. Francis accompanied him to Thonon where the Bishop received them most kindly. Upon his arrival at Thonon, the Archbishop informed the parishoners of the love and solicitude the Holy Father felt for his newly-gained children of the Chablais. In response, the people expressed their deep gratitude for the Pope's paternal interest and acknowledged him as their only head of the Catholic church. When Monsignor had finished his enquiry, he forwarded a most favorable report to Rome. "The number of converts which has grown by a thousand since last Easter is now twelve thousand. At Thonon, out of two thousand souls, five hundred communicants were counted at Paschal time; every day new abjurations are being received."

* * *

In the spring of the following year while Francis was giving Lenten instructions in the Cathedral of Annecy, word reached him that his father, now in his 79th year, was dangerously ill. Francis left immediately for Chateau Sales where he fortified the brave old warrior with the last sacraments and spoke loving and consoling words of comfort.

"We must all die, dear father," he softly whispered. "These words may seem hard at first sound, but they are followed by a great happiness. Think, my father. It is in order to be with God that we die. Let us then be willing to go forward with great confidence under the standard of God's Providence, without yielding to fears. If we think of death with uneasiness, the thought will be more injurious than advantageous to us. Let us think on it with peace and tranquillity of mind, reposing on the bosom of Providence."

"Francis, my boy," said the sick man, "you are indeed one of my sweetest consolations. I have tried to live well so I should not be afraid of death."

"Too, dear father, you have always loved God unselfishly so He will never send you from His presence into exterior darkness which is prepared only for rebels to His light and His love. Rely, dear father, on the merits of our Lord's Passion.

[73]

God is so good, so sweet to those who love Him," murmured the kneeling priest.

"How can I ever sufficiently thank God for giving me such help in the person of you, my dear son? Never do I weary of hearing your sweet and gentle words about the good God."

"Now, dear father, before I leave you for the night I wish you to make not only your act of resignation, but to lovingly accept death and unite yours to that of Jesus Christ's. I do not doubt, my father, but that he who is grieved for having offended God, and accepts death willingly, in satisfaction for his sins, will immediately obtain pardon. Why waste so advantageous an occasion of honoring God, satisfying His Justice, discharging one's debts, and purchasing heaven?" concluded Francis as he rose and blessed his father.

The next day Francis returned to Annecy as the doctors had informed him that there was no immediate danger, Monsieur de Boisy might linger for some weeks. At Annecy, Francis resumed the Lenten conferences he had been obliged to interrupt.

A few evenings later, just as he was about to mount the pulpit, a messenger from Sales' castle hastened after Francis with a message from Madame de Boisy announcing the death of her husband. Sword in one hand, crucifix in the other, the grand old nobleman had quietly breathed his last in the presence of his devoted wife and two of his sons.

For a moment Francis fell on his knees in prayer then, fortified by Divine Assistance, he ascended the pulpit and preached with more than his usual fervor and skill. His sermon concluded, Francis added in tender words, "My friends, I have just received word that my dear father died but a few hours ago. You who knew and loved him in life, please remember him in his death."

With bowed head the speaker left the sanctuary and set off at once for Sales castle where he flung himself upon the dead body of his father and sobbed out his grief and sorrow in the bitter loss. After he had prayed for some time for the happy repose of his departed father's soul, he devoted himself to making funeral arrangements.

Two days later enormous crowds from every rank and file of life attended the burial Mass at the church in Thonon and the ceremonial of interment. When the Sales family returned to their estate, Francis consoled his mother, brothers and sister exhorting them to spiritualize their heavy sorrow. "Keep in mind," he urged them, "that while the bee makes honey, it often lives upon bitter juices; we have no better opportunity of making acts of resignation and meekness than when we are eating the bread of bitterness, and living in the midst of suffering."

At the end of the week Francis again set out for Annecy, completed his conferences and preached on Easter and the succeeeding Sundays.

On one of the Sundays during the Easter season when he was preaching on his ever-favorite subject, the love of God, his words sparkled with fervor and devotion as with exquisite delicacy he pictured the love of God for each individual soul. "Never was a more beautiful biography ever written than this biography of love, the love of the Master for souls," he suggested.

His audience, completely enraptured, suddenly witnessed a miracle. Francis was surrounded with an aura of light so brilliant that they could scarcely gaze upon his glowing features. God was indeed testifying the truth of his disciple's burning words!

Now, the excellence of Francis' preaching, supported by this visible sign of God's approval, was marked by wonderful results: sinners repented, enemies became reconciled and the luke-warm became more fervent.

Chapter VI

MASSES OF FLEUR-DE-LIS

ON the 25th of July, 1593, in the church of St. Denis, amid pomp, ceremony and masses of fleur-de-lis, Henry IV, one of the greatest of French kings, was embracing the Catholic faith.

Reginald de Beaume, Archbishop of Bourges, was assisted by nine bishops, and many, many members of the secular and regular clergy.

"Who are you?" questioned the Archbishop.

"The king," came the prompt response.

"What do you desire?" was the next question.

"To be received into the bosom of the Catholic, Apostolic and Roman church," answered Henry in a clear vioce.

"Do you absolutely and unflinchingly desire it?"

"Yes, with all my heart, I so desire," emphasized Henry as he knelt and made the stipulated profession of faith. The monarch then confessed, assisted at Mass and received Benediction. Now indeed, he was a living member of the one, holy, Catholic and apostolic church.

What a tumult of joy arose among the Parisians

who had pushed and pulled to gain entrance to the colorful, historic ceremony! In the sanctuary the celebrated Oriflamme, the consecrated banner of the Kingdom of France, waved and swayed as the vaulted cathedral roof rang with glad cries: "Hurrah for our king, long live our king!"

* * *

Now, nine years later, the whole scene of his reception was startlingly revived in Henry's memory as he knelt at Mass, in his gem-like chapel at Fontainebleau. Francis de Sales, Coadjutor of the Bishop of Geneva, was the celebrant, and his graceful reverent movements made a profound impression on the king as he contrasted the gentle, withal noble demeanor of this priest with the proud arrogant manner of the prelate of Bourges. "Truly," murmured Henry to himself, as the Mass ended, "Monsignor de Geneva (a title he used for Francis) is the phoenix of prelates. Others all have a weak side. With one it is low birth, with another little learning, a third is wanting the necessary piety. This priest has all qualities in the highest degree. He is of illustrious birth, rare learning and piety."

Later, meeting Francis in the Court of Adieux, and walking with him over the great blocks of stone pavement, he stopped abruptly at the foot of the unique Horseshoe staircase, leading to the castle's entrance and begged, "Stay with us here in Paris and Fontainebleau, Monsignor. I will give you a wealthier see, and a much better position than the one you hold under Charles Emmanuel."

"Sire," answered Francis, with a twinkle in his bright, blue eyes, "I have married a poor wife and cannot desert her for a rich one."

"Well, well," exclaimed the monarch, amused with Francis' ready answer, "it is unfortunate Henry IV was so late in discovering the witty Savoyard."

"I humbly entreat, your Majesty," continued Francis in his suave manner, "if you have any regard for me, and for the worthy Bishop of Geneva whose mouthpiece I am, to restore the liberty of Catholic worship in the Pays de Gex."

"Monsieur Villeroi is taking care of the affair for us. In a few days he should be able to advise us," answered Henry.

Francis well-knew that the astute statesman Villeroi was by no means favorable to the Bishop of Geneva's request and was purposing delaying the inquiries, and placing every possible obstacle to its accomplishment.

On Low Sunday, Francis preached before the King and Court assembled in the royal chapel of the Chateau. Henry had heard something of the priest's reputation as a speaker and was eager to verify it. "Perfection" was the subject Francis had selected, and it seemed to his enraptured audience that every word he uttered was an arrow dipped in the Blood of the Heart of Jesus, wounding the hearers with love for their Saviour.

"We hear so much talk about perfection," he stated, "and see so little of it practiced. Everyone has fashioned a perfection of his own . Some make it consist in austerity of manners, while others place it in mortification of the senses: to one the giving of alms is the cream of perfection, — for another the approaching to the sacraments: others will say that prayer makes a man perfect. All these are mistaken ideas, because causes and means are taken for their effects. As for myself, I know of no other perfection but that of loving God with our whole heart and our neighbor as ourselves."

"Charity," continued the speaker, "is the only tie of perfection among Christians. It is the only virtue which properly unites us to God and to our neighbors, and in charity our end consists. We only deceive ourselves when we form other plans of perfection. I beg of you to learn to look upon all the souls of men as resting in the heart of Our Saviour. Beholding them in that divine resting place, who can otherwise than love them and bear their imperfections? Who dares call them irritating or troublesome? Yes, your neighbor is there in the heart of the Saviour, and there so beloved and lovable that the Divine Lover dies there for love of him."

"A truly charitable love for our neighbor," declared the holy prelate, "is a rarer thing than one would think. It is like the few particles of gold which are found on the shores of the Tagus, among masses of sand."

"Whoever liveth not in charity," concluded Francis, "is dead, and whatever deeds are performed, not inspired by charity, no matter how seemingly good, are dead works, and are of no merit for eternity."

At dinner Henry remarked to his wife, Mary de Medici, 'the fat bankeress from Florence,' "Those who told me that this Savoyard was a great man were not wrong, I have never heard a more powerful speaker."

Turning then to the Duke of Sully, Henry gaily said, "I should like to get the Holy Father's permission to send this preacher to England. He could easily convert James I."

Once again Francis found himself flooded with offers of important bishoprics, costly gifts and other marks of royal favor. Tactfully but positively he refused each offer.

"Sire," he entreated Henry on one occasion, "I thank you with all my heart for the great kindnesses you have shown me. I cannot, however, accept your many and gracious favors."

The king courteously replied, with his delicate and ready tact, "Your modesty, Monsignor de Geneva, places you above me. I consider myself to be above those who court my favors, but I am beneath those who refuse them."

"Your majesty," pleaded Francis, who had just received word that Claude de Granier was dangerously ill, "you have often told me that you are more Catholic than your most Catholic subject. You say you will have no distinction between Huguenots and Catholics. You wish all to be good Frenchmen and live peaceably as fellow-citizens. Why then will you not give the people of Pays de Gex the liberty of conscience the rest of France enjoys?"

Touched by Francis' evident signs of grief over his Bishop's illness, and moved by the sincerity of his plea, Henry, with his ever-ready charm, said, "We grant your desire. I shall instruct Baron de Luz to re-establish the Catholic religion in Gex, without any further delay."

What an outcry was raised when the news was announced that the Bishop-elect was to leave for Annecy!

A Huguenot lady, Madame de Roscanis, the Madame de Sevigny of those days, had a remarkable reputation for wit and learning and drew a large following to her salon where charm, humor and repartee sparkled. A number of famous Catholic controversialists had tried, unsuccessfully, from time to time to convert her from the errors of Calvinism. Drawn by the praise of Francis' sermons which were then echoing in all parts of the city, Madame attended one of his talks, presented in the royal chapel. The marvelous skill with which the speaker depicted the Last Judgment so profoundly impressed her that she called upon the Bishop to discuss certain protestant doctrines with him. One interview led to another, until not only was Madame de Roscanis converted, but all the members of her distinguished family abjured Calvinism.

When this brilliant lady learned that Francis was soon leaving the French capital she hastened to plead with him to remain longer.

"My lord, you have here a fertile field, all ready for the harvest. Do not leave us so soon. Delay your departure for at least another month," she suggested.

"Any delay is too long for one who is in a hurry," quoted Francis.

"Perhaps, Seneca would have been more successful had he not uttered those words," promptly replied the learned lady. "Too, the cases are very different. Look at the numbers who have already abjured the Calvinist faith since you have been with us. You, my lord, are well-versed in the art of preaching; all you utter is savored with kindness and love — powerful weapons against heretics who are opposed to lengthy controversial words. Only yesterday, Cardinal de Perron remarked to me, 'God has given to Monsignor de Geneva the key that unlocks all hearts.' Reconsider the idea of remaining, my lord."

"My dear lady, duty calls me home to my own diocese now that my official business with his Majesty is being so successfully terminated. Perhaps, someday I shall again have the pleasure of visiting and preaching in Paris."

Marie de Medici, vain, haughty and vindictive, had been captivated by Francis de Sales' charm at their first meeting. His kindly interest in her on that occasion made her very happy as she seldom encountered sympathy and understanding in the

French Court. The holy prelate grasping her position at once had suggested that she busy herself in the corporal works of mercy, spiritual reading and that she even take lessons in French which she spoke so poorly. He urged her to interest herself in royal affairs so that she might become her husband's confidant, and not grieve over those in whom he confided. Louis, the Dauphin, though little more than a year old was already showing signs of obstinacy and stubbornness, and Francis foresaw and instructed Marie de Medici that unless she schooled both herself and her young son in the practice of heroic virtue there would be many a future tussle between Queen, King and Dauphin. Marie, grateful, had tried to subdue her cantankerous temper. In fact, for a time the domestic relations between Henry and Marie seemed so peaceful that people thought Henry must surely have ended his amorous fancies and resolved to settle down with Marie and Louis.

When Marie learned that Francis was leaving she summoned him to her presence.

"What shall we do without you, my lord?" she asked.

"Place all your confidence in God," he answered.

"Before you leave, Monsignor, I beg your blessing for my little son and for myself."

"I shall remember you and your anxieties in my prayers," promised Francis.

There had been only one tiny blemish to mar the visitor's pleasant sojourn in Paris.

It so happened that a formidable conspiracy had been fomented by the Duke of Savoy, the Duke of Bouillon, the Count of Auvergne and the King of Spain to kill Henry IV, and then to divide France among the great nobles. At the head of this rebellious group was Marshal de Bion, known as the 'lightning of France.' He it was who had fought, side by side, with Henry at the famous battle of Ivry and had reported the chivalrous incident that occurred before the battle.

"At supper that night before the battle," de Bion had stated, "Henry had spoken harshly to a German officer named Schomberg. While he was marshaling his troops for the fight the next morning, Henry stopped his horse before the officer. 'Monsieur de Schomberg,' he had said, 'I know your valor and ask your pardon, embrace me.'

'Ah, Sire,' cried the poor German, overcome by the great condescension of the King, 'Your Majesty wounded me yesterday, today you kill me.' "

For many years, de Bion, Baron de Lux, had been Henry's bosom friend so when the King learned of his treachery he exclaimed in amazement to the Duke of Sully, "I never loved anybody as I loved de Bion. I would have trusted my little son and my kingdom to him."

"Your Majesty, here again we find treason which began by being cautious betraying itself. Charles de Bion boasted 'Caesar or nothing.' At another time he was heard to say 'I will not die without seeing my head on a quarter-crown piece.' Well, his head will not go down in history on a coin, but his name will remain abhorred to ensuing ages. What a price is treachery," stated the Duke of Sully.

Someone had told the King that Francis was one of the conspirators. When the bishop learned that he had been reported to Henry as being in Paris an an emissary of the Duke of Savoy, in order to manage the conspiracy, he hastened to Louvre to seek an audience with Henry.

As soon as the King saw his visitor he guessed his errand and hastened to inform him that he did not credit the tales that were circulating about him.

"There is no need for you to justify yourself, Monsignor de Geneva," said Henry kindly, "for I have never suspected you. No matter what rumors have come to my ears, I knew you were innocent of all treachery."

"Your Majesty, never would I enter into a plot against you. You have overwhelmed me with kindnesses, your latest being discrediting the false reports about me. Be assured, my King, I shall always be loyal to you. Should I ever forget my sovereign, may God forget me."

*   *   *

It was with a happy heart that Francis left Paris, but his joy was short-lived. Word reached him on the evening of his second day's journey that Claude de Granier had passed to his eternal reward. Heavy sorrow turned the stars above his bent head "into mourners and every wind of heaven into a dirge."

"Truly," murmured Francis to his traveling companion, "as one of our French writers has stated, 'it is with sorrows as with countries, each man has his own.'"

CHAPTER VII

GOLDEN JONQUILS

THE warm October sun was pouring its full flood of golden rays on the little group eating luncheon at Chateau Sales.

"My dear children, said Madame de Boisy as she glanced at the happy group, "I have some delightful news for you."

"Oh, I love surprises, mother, do tell us at once," exclaimed little Jeanne, the baby of the family.

"Guess who is coming to visit us for a few days?"

"Gasparde and her husband?" questioned Bernard.

"Guess again," suggested the mother.

"Not Francis, mother?" asked John Francis, his face alight with joy.

"Mother, is Francis coming home?" interrupted Jeanne, radiant and alert.

"Yes, he is coming to visit with us before he makes his retreat."

"How perfect. It is months since we have seen him," said Bernard as he reached for a smooth russet-brown pear.

"Does everyone who becomes a Bishop have to make a retreat in preparation for the big event?" asked John Francis who was seriously contemplating studying for the priesthood.

"I believe so. As I recall it's a twenty day retreat, too. You can ask Francis when you see him. Jeanne, take a piece of fruit. It's good for you."

"I wonder if Francis will think I'm a big girl, now?" murmured Jeanne as she obeyed her mother's suggestion.

What delightful hours were spent those charming October days as mother and son exchanged notes and comments on the "cheerful yesterdays" of the past six months. Too, Francis spent some time in inspecting the estate with Gallois, visited one day at La Roche with Gasparde who had married the Lord of Cornillon and was graciously dispensing hospitality at her lovely chateau, and stayed with Louis whose little son, Charles Augustus, was a constant source of novelty and delight. Francis found many occasions for complimenting Louis, Lord of Thuille, who had already gained fame for his skill in reconciling those at variance, and lastly he attempted to answer any and every question proposed to him by John Francis who was avaricious for detailed information about the priesthood.

Before he entered upon his long silence Francis wrote a filial letter of thanksgiving to the Pope, stating in part:

"While I was on my return journey from Paris I received word that our Bishop of Geneva had ended his days. No greater loss could have been inflicted upon our providence. At no time during his twenty-five years as Bishop did he ever deprive Geneva of his presence; partly by his own labors, partly by the work of others be brought back no fewer than twenty-five thousand erring sheep to the fold of Christ.

This noble prelate, Holy Father, asked not long ago that I, who was dear to him by no bonds of flesh and blood, should be appointed his coadjutor and successor, a request which, to his intense delight, was granted to him by your Holiness's kindness. It only remains for me, therefore, to commit myself and my charge with full confidence to the care of Divine Providence. To you, most holy Father, I offer the deepest thanks for the immense benefits which your apostolic munificence has bestowed upon me. I can find no way of making a return for such kindness other than by offering you my most grateful and heartfelt goodwill, which I dedicate wholly and entirely to your Holiness's services and pleasure."

Then it was November and time for the great silence or solitude when his soul might retire to "the audience chamber of God." He began his retreat by making a general confession to Father Fourier, S. J. and the remaining days were spent in interviews with his Jesuit director, in prayer and in consideration of his future needs.

During this time Francis exclaimed, "How I long that this heart which God has given to me should be inseparably bound to Him. I have so great a desire to advance in holy love that I am going to impose upon myself a rule of life."

Having consulted Father Fourier he drew up the following guide:

First, in regard to dress, I will not wear rich garments but they must be clean and suitably made. In church, house and town, as far as circumstances permit, I shall always wear a biretta. I shall wear only the pastoral ring on my finger and no expensive, perfumed gloves.

Secondly, in regard to the household, I will not have a suite of attendants. There will be a secretary, two serving-men, a cook with his scullion and a footman. None of these men will wear plumes, nor swords, nor clothes of bright colors. I will have no women servants.

Thirdly, in regard to meals, the episcopal table

should be moderate and frugal, yet at the same time properly served and well-prepared. For half the time during dinner and supper some pious book shall be read aloud. The rest of the time shall be devoted to conversation. Dinner shall be at ten, supper at six. On fast days, dinner will be at eleven and collation at seven.

Fourthly, in regard to devotions, I will offer up the Holy Sacrifice of the Mass each morning at nine o'clock unless hindered by extreme necessity. In the morning after the customary prayers I shall meditate for the space of an hour. I shall try to keep myself always in the presence of God and I shall invoke Him on every occasion. I shall recite the Office standing, or on my knees. After Vespers I shall say the rosary; on feast-days I will say Vespers in choir. I shall go to confession every second or third day to the most capable confessor I shall most conveniently find. Finally, I shall make an eight days' retreat every year.

So that this rule of life might have the character of an external command, and that he might profit by the grace of obedience, Francis submitted it to his director, Father Fourier, who not only sincerely approved of it but affixed his signature to it. Throughout his entire future life Francis was faithful to its observance except in extreme cases when precise times for the performance of his episcopal duties made an alteration necessary.

* * *

On the eighth of December, in the old family, stone church of Thorens, Francis de Sales was consecrated Bishop of Geneva by Vespasian Grimaldi, formerly Archbishop of Vienna. Under Madame de Boisy's direction and skill the little church was transformed into a veritable bower of beauty and color. Rich tapestries covered the walls, the armorial bearings of the House of Sales, surmounted by a gold cross, a mitre and a green hat adorned the sanctuary and masses of golden jonquils and ivory-petalled jasmine, grouped about the high altar, perfumed the church. The combined choirs of the cathedral and of the collegiate church of Our Lady had charge of the music on this auspicious occasion and over three hundred nobles represented their social order. The ceremony began early in the morning.

When the mitre was placed on his head Francis felt that he should watch over his senses with the greatest care and that he should do all in his power to explain the Scriptures to his little flock. The gloves suggested another thought—the necessity of good works. In turn, the ring reminded him that he must be faithful to the Holy See, and the pectoral cross impressed upon his mind that it was his duty to sustain the weak, admonish sinners, convert heretics and, in short, to carefully perform the corporal and spiritual works of mercy. Sandals and buskins were a reminder that he should follow in the footsteps of His Master, through smooth and rough ways, in the pursuit of his sheep.

A miracle marked the consecration of Francis. As he was kneeling in humble prayer, afire with divine love, his gentle countenance appeared radiant like a Seraphim's and he saw clearly and distinctly the Blessed Trinity, the Blessed Virgin and the holy apostles, Peter and Paul. Now it was that the deep piety and intense fervor of Francis, augmented by the graces of the ceremony, shone with even greater brilliancy and luster. On this day Francis resolved to devote himself unswervingly to the service of God, and to love Him daily more and more.

Long before the uncouth swain in mantle blue had even touched his oaten lute the newly-consecrated Bishop was off "to fresh woods and pastures new." His entry into the cathedral city was a progress of triumph! All the nobles from the neighboring country and four of the Counsellors met him at the outskirts of Annecy and accompanied him to the Church of Our Lady of Compassion where representatives from the Jesuits, Franciscans, Dominicans and Benedictine Orders together with the secular clergy and people of Annecy awaited him.

What a picture to be recored on maguey! The rich gleam and sheen of shirt, doublet and hose, the flash of silver swords and scabbards, the warm, rich silks, satins and woolens of the ladies, blending into the blacks, browns and whites of the religious habits, and in the midst of all stood the tall fair Bishop clad in his colorful episcopal robes.

From the church of Our Lady the procession moved to the cathedral where Francis made a solemn entry and prostrated himself before the Blessed Sacrament. Then bells from all the churches sang their sweet, celestial songs of jubilee and Francis was conducted to the episcopal chair where he sat and listened to a glowing sermon on his own virtues. With rare humility and fitting dignity he graciously responded to the warm words of praise remarking, in part, "I am happy in the thought that the Blessed Virgin of the Sovereign Pastor, should introduce me as a shepherd into the fold of Her Son, on this day of the week, especially consecrated and dear to her."

Again the bells pealed forth in triumphal chorus

as the mighty words of the Te Deum sung by all visiting clerics, mounted with the fragrant smoke of the incense to the very vaults of heaven where God's benediction fell like dew on the newly-installed Bishop, and mingled with his first episcopal blessing on his people.

* * *

Claude de Granier, due to the meagerness of his resources (the only money found in his home after his death was the sum of threepence) had not lived in a pretentious residence, but had rented a small dwelling opposite the cathedral. Now, many of the new bishop's friends wanted to change this arrangement.

"One of the first things your lordship must do is to purchase a fitting episcopal residence," advised Monsieur la Comte.

"I shall be only too happy to secure a suitable dwelling for you," offered Monsieur Benoit. "Perhaps, you will inspect a place I have in mind. I shall have my coachman stop by for you tomorrow and we can see the place together."

"No, no, thank you kindly," Francis hastily answered. "I do not desire another residence. I am very happy with the one I am in. Too," he added, with a merry twinkle in his bright blue eyes, "It is pleasant to know that I do not own a home of my own and that my landlord can evict me whenever he so desires."

In keeping with the spirit of poverty, he was almost Franciscan in this respect, and with his small income in mind (1,000 crowns yearly) he proceeded to organize his household which quickly became a model establishment. His rule of life guided him in the selection of servants and attendants. Care was taken that their conversation and bearing were such as became an episcopal palace and each hour of the day had its allotted task. Francis himself carefully watched over the spiritual and temporal welfare of his retainers and made it a rule that there should be silence from night prayers until after meditation the following morning.

One evening, without noticing what he was doing, one of the two priests living at the palace, began to hum the melody of a psalm. The Bishop, leaving his room, quietly sought the singer. "What are you doing, Father Michael?" he asked. "This is not the time for singing the praises of God."

For the reception of visitors, Francis had rooms richly furnished and attractively decorated, these he called "the Prince-Bishop apartments"; for himself he chose a small room, furnished in the plainest manner, containing several chairs, a bed, a table and a few of his favorite books, oil for his lamp of prayer. This place he called "Francis' room." In this abode of peace and quiet Francis governed with mildness and gentleness.

Early in January, not believing in the adage that "what cannot be cured must be endured" Francis began a campaign against an abuse which had gained remarkable headway in Annecy in connection with the observance of St. Valentine's day. It was of long-standing custom that young men and young women should meet on February 14th and that the names of those present should be printed in gold on pieces of satin. These were placed in an urn and the pieces of satin with the ladies' names were drawn by the young men who wore the bits of ribbon over their hearts as a sort of talisman and paired off with the lady herself for the year. The young man was to be so devoted to his valentine that he was to escort her to balls, accompany her to various social functions and to remember her with costly and appropriate gifts at certain times of the year. At Annecy, this custom had been adopted by the younger married group and it frequently led to misunderstandings and quarrels between husbands and wives.

For several Sundays the Bishop preached against

this custom. Naturally, there were a number who resented this interference in one of their greatest pleasantries. Francis then proceeded by public edict, to ban the custom of taking valentines.

Great was the storm of indignation which arose. Those who had formerly whispered against the Bishop's action now uttered loud and lengthy disapproval of the ban.

No whit disconcerted, Francis responded to those who begged him to remove the edict, "We are stronger than those who are making so much noise. We have God on our side. We will have no valentines this year, but we shall have peace and order and morality."

To a group of young girls he promised, "I shall undertake to supply you with a different type of valentine."

In fulfillment of this statement he sent to every family where there were young girls a number of tickets, each bearing the name of a particular saint, a special virtue and a quotation from the Scriptures. He ordered that these tickets be drawn by lot and that the recipient take the saint drawn, as a model for the ensuing year and strive to practice the virtue enjoined.

On all the lenten Fridays that followed the feast of St. Valentine Francis preached to the members of the Confraternity of the Holy Cross and during Holy Week wearing the rough garb of the organization he followed the procession of the Confraternity on Maundy Thursday to all the altars of repose in Annecy.

During the early part of the pentecostal season Francis made plans for a Synod to be held at Annecy in the fall as he was both eager and anxious to meet the priests of his diocese. In October, when all the priests had assembled, the Bishop divided his diocese into twenty districts, over each of which he placed a superintendent who was obliged every six months to visit the clergy of his district at their own homes and to send in a detailed account of the visitation to the Bishop. Francis emphasized a strict observance of the regulations of the Council of Trent regarding dress, prayers and services and he impressed upon them the necessity of always carrying with them the catechism of the Council of Trent, stressing the importance of holding catechism, Sunday-schools and preaching the word of God. It was decided at this meeting that each year a Synod should be held at Annecy, preferably during the month of October.

CHAPTER VIII

ROSEMARY FOR REMEMBRANCE

FRANCIS' days now slipped by as swiftly and smoothly as the Rhone with its silvery train. The dark clouds that had threatened around St. Valentine's Day, at Francis' gentle and courageous touch, showed in late fall of the same year only a silvery lining. It was at this time that the Mayor and aldermen of Dijon, having heard Francis' praises as a speaker sung far and wide, invited him to visit their city and give a series of Advent conferences. It was not, however, until the early days of 1604 that Francis asked and secured both Clement's and Charles Emmanuel's permission to leave Annecy for two months and to give the Lenten sermons in Dijon.

As a preparation for these conferences Francis retired to Sales' castle to make a short retreat. Here part of his time was spent in prayer and meditation, part in study. One morning while he was meditating in the chapel of St. Sebastin a marvelous thing happened to him — he received a sudden illumination from the Holy Ghost which shed upon his soul a flood of light so bright and clear concerning the truths of faith and the dispensations of graces that he later wrote in his notes:

"Oh God, my soul finds nothing hard to believe among the effects of Thy divine love: the beauty of our holy faith so ravishes me, that I fairly die for love of it and I am convinced that I ought to lock up so precious a gift of God in a heart all perfumed with love. When our mind, raised above all natural light begins to see the sublime truths of faith, Oh dear Lord, what joy and happiness. The soul finds pleasure in hearing the prayer of her heavenly Spouse and it is sweeter to her than the honey of human science, or in seeing His face, not indeed in the full splendor of the noon-day but in the feeble light of the dawn. Oh, what great joy comes to the soul from the light of faith! The learned Plato never experienced this, nor did the eloquent Demosthenes. Those happy disciples of Emmaus said, on hearing the words of faith: 'Was not our heart burning within us while He spoke to us on the way?' Now, if the divine truths afford us so much genuine pleasure when they are presented to us only in the obscure light of faith, oh God, what will it be when we contemplate them in the noon-day brightness of eternal glory?

When we shall arrive in the heavenly Jerusalem

and the King of Glory shall show us the marvels of heavenly truth and when we shall see clearly what we have believed here below, oh what ravishing delight, what admiration, what sweetness and what love we shall experience. 'Never,' we shall cry out in our transports of joy, 'never would we have thought that these truths could give us such delight.' "

Francis concluded his thoughts on faith by this beautiful prayer. "Live Jesus in Whom I believe, live Holy Church to which I adhere! Oh mother of the children of God, never shall I separate from thee; in thee I wish to die."

A second day, when in prayer, Francis saw in spirit, by divine inspiration, Madame Jane Frances Fremiot de Chantal who was destined by God to be an instrument for leading many souls to holiness. An inner voice whispered to Francis that one day he was to become the founder of an Order of Nuns and that the lady clothed in the black dress of a widow was to assist him in his foundation. The way that this Order was to increase and multiply was shown to him by two symbols: the one was a tree, planted in a valley from the depths of which it grew until it overtopped the surrounding mountains; the other was a fountain of sweet water, tiny at its source but ever flowing in a widening course until it divided and spread over the land in several fair streams and noble rivers."

In late February, on a day heavy with the promise of rain and lightning, the Bishop of Geneva arrived in Dijon. Here he was welcomed by a large number of ecclesiastics and several of the town's leading citizens who escorted him to the apartments which had been prepared for him.

At Dijon, as at Fontainebleau, Francis found himself surrounded by large, enthusiastic audiences. Catholics and Protestants who came to listen to his eloquent and brilliant talks were deeply impressed by the earnestness of the saintly preacher and by the charmingly refreshing illustrations he borrowed from nature to stress his points. In fact, numerous Catholics led more fervent lives and many Protestants were converted.

Many of Francis' free hours were spent in visiting the poor in their homes and the sick in the hospitals. Too, it was in the hospitals that he enjoyed saying Mass, hearing confession and administering Extreme Unction as he felt that the sick were in special need of spiritual consolations.

On one of his many visits to Hotel Dieu, Francis met Abbe Crillon who voiced his surprise at meeting Francis so often, "How is it, my Lord," he asked, "that you manage to find time in the midst of your short stay in our city to visit this hospital so frequently?"

"I am partial to sick people," responded the Bishop in his affable manner. "Long ago, I learned that sickness schools those who visit or wait upon the sick to mercy, and it trains the sick to an affectionate patience. The former stand at the foot of the Cross with Our Lady and St. John, the sick person is on that very Cross of Our Savior, whose suffering it imitates."

After a few cordial words in regard to the Abbe's robust health, Francis turned from him to enter the room of a poor, young woman in whom he was interested.

Mademoiselle Pate's thin, ashen-hued cheeks lighted with joy as she welcomed her caller. "You are most kind to visit me so often, my lord. Your calls are the bright 'purple patches' in the dark and dreary days," she said.

"And how are the pains today?" asked Francis.

"Worse than usual, I believe. I cannot even pray as long as I wish," she discouragingly replied.

"Do not worry yourself, my child, because you are kept to your bed, and thus prevented from indulging in prayer. To bear the rod of Our Saviour is a favor as great as that of communing with Him in prayer. Be sure of that," encouraged the kindly visitor.

"What a tonic your words are. I do so try to be resigned, but it is hard."

"But resignation brings peace of heart, my dear. Now, obey your doctor faithfully. When he forbids any practice of devotion, or fasting, or even prayer, unless it be aspirations, I beg of you most earnestly, to be scrupulously obedient, for such are the commands of God. Try to think, when your suffering is most intense, that the very angels of heaven envy you the boon of being able to suffer for Our Lord. They themselves have never had such an opportunity."

"Will you give me your blessing, my lord?" asked the sick girl.

"Gladly," answered Francis, "and I shall pray that before the feast of Easter you will be up and able to take part in its joyous celebration. God bless you, my dear child!"

One evening as Francis was preaching with his usual skill and fervor he noticed in the audience a lady dressed in deep mourning whom he immediately recognized as the person he had seen in a vision some months earlier.

"She is my sister," answered Archbishop-elect

Andre Fremiot, when he was questioned by the
Bishop of Geneva.

* * *

Jane Frances, Fremiot, Baroness de Chantal, was
the daughter of Benigne Fremiot, a judge of the
parliament of Burgundy. From her earliest years
Jane Frances had evidenced a great love for Jesus
Christ and an intense distaste for the Huguenot
religion. When in her 'teens she had married
Christophe de Rabutin, Baron de Chantal, and
for eight delightful years they had lived at Bourbilly, the family estate, where she devoted herself
to three things: the service of God, the good pleasure of her husband and the management of her
household. The order and saving which Madame
de Chantal maintained consistently during her
years at Bourbilly were so successful that she not
only liquidated all the debts with which the house
was burdened but took care that all running expenses were below the family income. Though she
was economical in managing affairs on the estate she
gave generously in charity to the poor. Not only
were her benefactions for the poor and needy who
would come to the chateau from a radius of fifteen
or twenty miles, but she always managed a certain
amount of quiet alms-giving to those whose families

were too proud or respectable to indulge in begging but were in dire need of assistance.

Religious though she was, the Baroness was never a nuisance to anyone. She always placed God first, but after her duties to Him came her husband's needs. She loved him so devotedly and sincerely that she did everything possible to please him. If guests happened to be staying at the chateau, and they frequently entertained, she was a perfect hostess, gracious, charming and entertaining. To please her cherished husband she wore beautiful, rich gowns; when he was away her dress became more simple than many of her servants'.

Six children were born to the Baron and Baroness during eight years of their residence at Bourbilly. Two of these children died in infancy, the other four lived interesting, eventful lives. All days are not the same, and one sad day dark tragedy entered the Bourbilly household and upset "the even tenor of the days." The Baron and his cousin Louis d'Anlezy, were on a shooting expedition and as they made their way through the woods a branch caught the trigger of Louis' weapon and Baron de Chantal fell, mortally wounded by the accidental shot in his thigh. Physicians were sent for in haste, but the Baron died after a few days of intense suffering.

Madame de Chantal and her children then spent the greater part of the time living with the father-in-law, a disagreeable old widower of seventy-five. Deprived of earthly support, and realizing that God alone was unchangeable, Jane Frances decided to belong body and soul to Jesus Christ, to live for Him alone. As she busied herself in educating her children, in reading and in caring for the sick and the poor she prayed constantly for the divine will to manifest Itself to her.

Frequently, on the long winter evening she would gather her children about her and talk to them about God. "His will is always beautiful, dear children. We must see His hand in every happening," she would say as she encouraged them to place all their confidence in Him.

Finally God, in answer to her earnest prayers, granted Jane Frances an extraordinary vision. One morning as she was taking one of her solitary walks and praying to God for guidance she saw before her, at the foot of the hill, a prelate dressed in cassock and rochet, with a biretta upon his head. Later she was to know this religious as Francis de Sales. As she gazed in astonishment she heard a voice say, "This is the guide, loved by God and by men, in whom you are to place your confidence." Immediately the figure disappeared and her soul was overwhelmed with deepest consolations.

Upon another occasion while she was engaged in prayer in the chateau's chapel, God gave her a vision of a large crowd of maidens and widows who were moving towards her. "You shall have this generation: they shall be to me a chosen flock," whispered our Lord, and later He told Jane Frances that she should enter upon the ways of peace through the gate of St. Claud.

Early in 1604, President Fremiot, Jane Frances' father, head of Dijon's parliament had invited his daughter to visit him and attend a series of Lenten conferences which the illustrious Bishop of Geneva had consented to preach. Jane Frances had accepted the invitation with delight, and the first night she heard the distinguished speaker she recognized him as the ecclesiastic of her vision, whom God had promised to her as a director.

* * *

The Archbishop-elect invited Francis to dine with him and his father, President Fremiot, the next evening and to meet the Baroness de Chantal. Francis was delighted to accept the pleasing invitation.

The following evening, introductions over, both

Francis de Sales and Jane Frances de Chantal felt that a strong, luminous, spiritual bond was being forged at once between their souls. From that very hour began a perfect union, constant, angelic, beautiful, a union seldom achieved on earth, utterly pleasing in the sight of God and of man.

"I am sure," remarked Andre Fremiot, after the Bishop and President Fremiot had departed, "that you found the Bishop of Geneva to be no "Reed shaken by the wind."

"Never," replied his delighted sister, "have I talked to anyone who was so filled with unswerving love for God's glory and the salvation of souls. Truly, my brother, he is an angel of God."

"He possesses a most unusual combination, utmost humility marked by noble refinement," mused the Archbishop-elect. "I do believe he is a chosen soul."

"Hereafter," remarked Jane Frances with a quizzical glance at her tall brother, "I shall take every opportunity of meeting this saintly prelate. When he dines at father's as I am sure he will, I shall be a member of the President's household; when he dines at the Archbishop's, I, my dear Andre, shall be among those present at your table."

Andre Fremiot, delighted with the beautiful friendship between the Bishop of Geneva and his dear sister, and happy that Jane Frances looked more rested and at peace than she had since the death of her husband, often invited the two to dine at his episcopal palace. Then it was that intimate, charming, soul-revealing conversations took place.

One evening the subject of portraits was introduced. A famous French artist had arrived in Dijon to paint portraits of two of the leading citizens. He was received with great acclaim and many hastened to him to arrange for sittings.

"I have known great servants of God who would not allow their portraits to be painted, imagining that their doing so involved some degree of vanity; what are your thoughts on this subject, my lord?" asked Andre.

"I have never made any objection to having my portrait taken, when I have been asked to do so," answered Francis with his charming nâivete.

Jane Frances glanced at the speaker in surprise. "I am rather astonished at your answer," she said to the Bishop.

"Why refuse people our portraits, my dear Baroness? If we see our books, which are the portraits of our minds, in the hands of our fellow-men, why grudge them the picture of our countenance, if it contribute anything to their satisfaction?" asked the wise prelate.

Andre nodded his head. "Yes, as usual, you have answered most judiciously," he stated. "Quite a remarkable way of looking at the matter, indeed, quite remarkable."

Another time a guest at President Fremiot's table remarked that taverns were nothing but dens of brigands. Francis was displeased with this statement but realized that neither time nor circumstance were appropriate to reprimand the speaker. He adroitly avoided further condemnation of innkeepers by the following anecdote:

"I recall the story of a Spanish palmer, whose pocket was not surfeited with money. He had halted at an inn where, after having been very poorly fared, he was so exorbitantly charged that he called on heaven and earth to witness the bad usage he had received. On leaving the tavern, in most upset and violent state of mind, he noticed at the other side of the square another inn, and a cross standing between the two. The sight infuriated him still more and he exclaimed, 'Truly, this is Calvary, and they have placed the cross of our Lord between two thieves,' meaning the two innkeepers. Now, the master of the inn opposite to which he had stayed was at his tavern door and heard the remark. Very civilly he asked the pilgrim in what way he had offended him and why he should be called a thief. The latter had more wit about him than his appearance suggested, and quickly rejoined, 'Hush! hush! hush! brother, you are the good thief.' Which meant of course, that as there was a thief on each side of the cross of our Saviour, a good and bad one, the present innkeeper was the good one as he had not harmed the traveler."

The Bishop concluded by saying, "The Spanish pilgrim drowned his grief in his gentle wit: yet it is necessary to avoid sweeping condemnations of peoples and trades."

"Have you never been charged double and treble the price of a night's lodging?" asked Andre Fremiot, still chuckling at the witty palmer's answer.

"My dear Archbishop, it is not only for the night's lodging that we pay; we must take into account the inn-keepers' cares, troubles, watching at night and the general good will they manifest to us. Indeed, there is no pay enough for all that."

"I have known some holy old inn-keepers," remarked President Fremiot as his mind dipped into the past.

"In my opinion, theirs is one of the best situations in which to serve God in their neighbor's person, and to advance rapidly towards heaven. Such men are continually employed in works of mercy, although, like physicians, they take pay for their services," concluded Francis.

One rainy afternoon, as the Baroness was seated before an open fireplace with her brother she turned the conversation to the Beatitudes.

"Blessed are the peacemakers has always been my favorite," answered Andre when questioned by his sister as to his favorite Beatitude.

"Blessed are the poor in spirit has been my motto from the early days when I learned the eight of them," stated Jane Frances.

"Let us ask the Bishop of Geneva which his favorite one is," suggested Andre. "He is dining with us tonight."

"My dear brother, I am willing to ask, though I can tell you right now that his answer will be the second. 'Blessed are the meek.' He surely has taken that for his guide."

Great was the astonishment when Francis answered the Baroness' question that evening after dinner. "Blessed are they that suffer persecution for justice sake!" he answered promptly.

Andre glanced at his sister with a teasing smile. "Why, my lord, do you think that the most perfect?" he questioned.

"The life of those who are persecuted for justice sake is hidden in God with Jesus Christ, and becomes conformable to His image; for was not He persecuted all His life for justice sake, albeit He followed it in all its perfection? Such people appear sinful while they are just; dead while they live; poor, yet they are rich; fools, and are wise: in a word, despised before men, they are dear to God with whom they will live forever."

"My lord," said Jane Frances with a nod to her brother, "I have a confession to make. I assured Andre, only this afternoon, that I was positive that your favorite Beatitude was 'blessed are the meek.' How little one should judge another."

On one of his last visits to President Fremiot's home, Francis was happy to learn from Jane Frances that she had precisely the same object in life as he. Led by the inspiration of the Holy Ghost, she begged the saintly Bishop to direct her. Francis, after prayer and due consideration, accepted the charge, and capably trained and fashioned her noble soul so that she might be fully prepared for the great work in which she was to assist him.

As the time for his departure from Dijon drew near, a storm of protest arose. The citizens, loud in their approbation of his marvelous works and sermons, and of the excellent example he gave of making himself 'all to all' for Christ's sweet sake, voiced poignant regrets that he was leaving their city so soon.

A delegation from the city Council and some of the leading nobles of the city waited on him the morning before he left Dijon.

"We are under many obligations to your lordship," stated the spokesman of the gathering.

"I have enjoyed and profited by my days in your lovely city," courteously responded the Bishop.

"Yor unusual sermons have given us food for thought for many days," said Monsieur de Cesre.

"Too, your noble examples of patience and charity and your superb evenness of temper have aroused our deepest admiration and have stamped themselves indelibly on our memories," said another councilman.

"I am only one of God's instruments," humbly stated the Bishop. "I am happy to have been of some use to you."

"As a token of our sincere esteem and a memento of our gratitude we beg you to accept this silver service," said the Mayor as he stepped forward to present a beautifully wrapped gift, fastened with a sprig of fragrant rosemary.

Francis, pleased with their sincere expressions

of appreciation, was firm in refusing the costly gift.

"I did not come among you to sell the word of God. I can not possibly accept this present though I sincerely appreciate your kind thought of me," he pleaded.

Madame de Crecy, witnessing the esteem of her fellow-citizens for this holy prelate and admiring his gentle refusal of the present, playfully said, "You are a thief, my lord."

Surprised, Francis turned to her and asked, "How is that, my dear lady?"

"You are robbing us all of our hearts and will carry them away to Annecy with you," she explained.

"Very well," Francis said with a delightful smile, "in place of a gift of silver I shall carry the gift of your hearts."

"If you must leave us, would that we might carry you in our arms to Geneva," cried the devoted people.

"Parting is indeed 'sweet sorrow' when it is from such good friends," remarked Francis as he imparted his episcopal Benediction to the kneeling group.

Chapter IX

A CROWN OF LAUREL

"GREAT souls are portions of eternity." Of the many great, noble-hearted souls living in the seventeenth century one of those whose name was to ring down the ages in clear, mellifluous tones was Francis de Sales, Bishop of Geneva. In the words of a Spanish writer "grace did not destroy his rich wealth of natural charm, it served to enhance it."

Francis' days were full days. Upon his return from Dijon in the late spring of 1604, in addition to attending to his own spiritual exercises and his episcopal duties, which embraced Mass, administering the sacraments, holding diocesan synods, and making the visitation of his whole diocese, he managed to find time to write several books of merit, establish an academy and keep up a voluminous correspondence which increased with the years. It was in particular in the steady correspondence between Francis and Jane Frances de Chantal that 'heart spoke to heart.' In these beautiful, old French letters one finds charm of expression, variety of thoughts and sentiments, practical wisdom, solid piety, and safe and prudent rules for growth in holiness, all scintillating with deep, glowing love for God, shining "like butterflies in the glowing sun, or fire flies in the deepening dusk." Fortunately about nine hundred of Francis' letters have been preserved for our admiration and edification.

Too, ever present in the Bishop's mind was the vision of the Order with which God willed him, with the aid of Baroness de Chantal, to adorn earth and heaven. Francis realized that here he must prudently follow his own preaching 'make haste slowly' as God in His own good time would provide for the soul that relied upon His aid for "no one trusts in God without reaping the fruits of his confidence." Whenever he had done the utmost for the success of an undertaking he left the rest to God. In fact, just before the foundation of his religious Order, Francis wrote to Jane de Chantal, "I do not see any chance for the establishment of our institute, but I am sure that God will crown our efforts with success."

How the holy Bishop loved to visit his ever-growing flock. Beloved by all, he made himself a father to all. In him the poor found support and the sinners found mercy. His mildness and gentleness won the hearts of even the most hardened. In Chapter he urged his priests to remember the parable of the Good Samaritan and to imitate him in pouring oil and wine into the wounds of the poor wayfarer, or sinner. "No sauce was ever spoiled by too much sugar" he was often heard to say, and "there is no soil so ungrateful as not to bear fruit when a kindly hand cultivates it."

Somedays as the bishop made his way down the streets of Annecy he found himself surrounded by admiring groups of children who formed a colorful little cortege as, matching their tiny footsteps to his, they escorted him on his round of pastoral calls. Ecstatically they exclaimed over the charming little holy cards of baby Jesus and the images of Blessed Mother and the saints which the generous bishop always presented when they arrived at the episcopal residence at the conclusion of the afternoon's calls.

In February of 1605, at the insistence of the people of La Roche who felt that they had a special claim upon Francis because he had received part of his education in their college, he left Annecy and traveled on foot to the little college town to preach a series of Lenten instructions. Here he applied himself to his activities with the same enthusiasm and energy that he displayed in the larger cities. Besides his work of preaching, he offered to hear confessions as often as penitents desired to go, and allotted parts of Wednesdays and Fridays to catechetical lessons. Two days a week were set apart for conferences for the clergy. At these meetings Francis explained ceremonials of the Liturgy, stressed points of moral theology and concluded each session by exhortations on the duties and virtues of the priesthood. On Sundays, he held Confirmation, and Ordination was conferred on three different occasions during his brief stay in La Roche. At one of these times G. Rolland, Francis,' ever-faithful attendant and friend, was ordained.

It so happened one morning that a poor man, Monsieur Martin, who had been deaf and dumb from his birth, and earned his livelihood by performing small domestic tasks in any house where he might find employment, called at the residence where Francis was staying. The holy Bishop was immediately touched by the man's misfortune and that very day, by means of signs, undertook the deaf mute's religious education. In a few weeks, because of the Bishop's kindness, tact and patience, Monsieur Martin was sufficiently instructed so that he was able to make his first Holy Communion during the Easter-tide.

Before he left La Roche, Francis decided to make
Monsieur Martin a permanent member of his household. When the news leaked out, as news always
does, some of Francis' best friends were consider-
ably disconcerted.

"Why should you burden yourself with a man
who will be practically useless?" they asked.

"The more God has afflicted him, the more I
ought to pity him," answered Francis, with his
tolerant smile. "Were we in his place would we
not appreciate kindness from others?"

"You will find yourself sorely tried by his help-
lessness," they predicted.

"Then he will help me to practice the virtue of
charity," calmly answered Francis.

* * *

In the fall of 1605 and the spring of 1606, Francis made a visitation of his whole diocese, over hill
over dale, through storms and mid sunshine, undergoing excessive fatigue and often in great danger
in the Alpine districts which formed the greater
part of the field of his labors. In all places he
preached, catechized, administered the sacraments,
visited the sick and distributed alms. All the time
he was busily engaged in saving the souls of others,
he drew lessons for his own profit, from the beauties

of the surrounding country-side and from the homely, simple lives of the poor.

When he arrived in the tiny village of Samoens, he found a terrible state of discord: its people, divided by partisan spirit, were filled with hate towards one another. Happily Francis had arrived in their midst during the octave of the Assumption and he made judicious use of this fact by relating to them the traditional story of Mary's assumption and concluded his talk with words torn from the depths of his heart, "My dear people, Mary died of love and we, we live in hate. She rose up to heaven, we, I fear, are going down to hell unless we amend our ways." He then burst into tears as he thought of the loss of this little hate-torn group, and hastily left the pulpit. His heart-broken words and sobs, unusual in one so mild and gentle, had a definite effect on the people. That very night numbers became reconciled and made fervent confessions.

The next evening after he had gone into the pulpit, Francis made the sign of the cross, as usual, and then pronounced only two words, "Jesus . . Mary." A soft silence followed. In a few moments he again repeated the two names and surrendering himself to sublime inspiration he spoke in soul-stirring words on the two sacred names:

"From the depths of your hearts pronounce the name of Jesus. It will spread a delicious balm over your souls. How happy we should be had we only Jesus in our understanding, only Jesus in our memories and only Jesus in our wills. Let us kiss our Saviour's wounds and say, 'Our hearts are calling for Thee, O God. We desire to gaze upon Thy sacred face!' Let us keep ourselves united to Jesus Christ, our eyes to look upon Him, our lips to praise Him, in fine our whole being to do what is most agreeable to Him. Now, the love for Jesus is almost inseparable from love for Mary. The more we love Jesus, the more we ought to love her who had given Him to us, whom He Himself has loved so much and whose glory is His own, for all her greatness is derived from Him. As God came to us through Mary, He desired that we should go to Him through her."

The impression these words made on Francis' audience was profound. The remaining inhabitants who had not become reconciled with their neighbors the evening before, now hastened to Francis to have him settle their points of difficulty. With his marvelous powers of justice and conciliation the current disputes were soon happily settled and the following day the Bishop left the little village which was enjoying a pleasant, refreshing peace.

From Samoens, Francis and his companion journeyed down the valley of the Giffre to the little town of Viuz in the vale of Boege. A week before the Bishop and his Abbe had arrived a most unfortunate accident had occurred near the little settlement. The incident, related to his lordship by an eye witness, made a most profound impression and Francis wrote of the tragedy to Madame de Chantal:

"My dear daughter,

Let me tell you of one incident, a true story, which makes me shiver with fear. A week before we arrived in the glacier country, a poor herdsman was wandering hither and thither over the ice-fields in search of a cow that strayed. Not taking sufficient care of his steps, he fell down a crevasse, a chasm about one hundred and fifty feet deep. No one would have known what had happened to him, were it not that his hat, falling from his head at the moment of the accident, had been left on the edge of the gulf, and so marked the place he had perished. One of his neighbors had himself lowered by means of a rope, in order to find him, and discovered him not only dead but covered with ice; and, in this state he put his arms around him and shouted for the others to pull him up, otherwise he himself would have died of cold. They pulled him up, therefore, holding in his arms the dead body of his friend, to which he afterwards gave Christian burial. What a spur for me, my dear daughter! This pastor who makes his way through such dangerous country for only one animal: this horrible fall, caused by the ardor of his quest, his attention fixed upon the object of his search and the tract of its wandering rather than upon his own steps and the place over which he is passing: the charity of the neighbor who goes down into the abyss to draw his friend from its depths! This country of ice, must it not, then, freeze with terror or rather should it not burn with love?"

When Francis finally returned to Annecy he had visited one hundred and eighty-five parishes.

The next task which needed his attention was the assembling of a report of his diocese which he was bound by oath to render to the Holy See every five years, either by going to Rome himself, or by sending someone in his place. After Francis had drawn up a comprehensive account of the clergy, churches, schools and religious houses in his diocese he wrote of his visitation and about the heretics who occupied part of his territory. The document being completed, he entrusted it to his brother Jean Francis who was to bear it to

Rome. With this report he gave Jean a letter to the Holy Father, stating the reasons which prevented his journeying to Rome at the time.

Young Canon de Sales, as brother and envoy of the learned and saintly Bishop of Geneva, was warmly and flatteringly welcomed in the Eternal City. The report on the diocese was read with avid interest and Cardinal Pamphili, who was commissioned to answer it, congratulated the Bishop on all the good he had accomplished in so short a time and promised that his several petitions should receive due consideration.

*   *   *

In the month of August on the twenty-first day, in the year 1608 Farncis de Sales wrote: "To-day I finish my forty-first year. Pray to Our Lord that He will make the rest of my age useful to His glory and to my own salvation."

As early as 1602 he had been gathering together material which he hoped would serve as a guide to perfection for men and women engaged in the occupations of ordinary family life. Since priests and monks wrote only for the clergy and convents, the result was that large numbers of people, living in the world deprived of suitable guidance, thought a life of sanctity and perfection as far removed from them as mind is above matter. In commenting

[129]

on the composition of "The Introduction to a Devout Life" Francis wrote to the Archbishop of Vienna in 1608: "It is a memorandum which I had composed for an excellent soul who had asked for my guidance." This soul, Madame de Charmoisy (wife of Monsieur de Charmoisy, a gentleman of the court of the Duke of Nemours, and a relative of Francis de Sales) showed the memorandum to Father Fourier, S. J., Rector of the Jesuit College of Chambery, who strongly urged its publication for general use. In August of the same year, Francis confided the printing of this work to Pierre Rigaud of Lyons, and early in the next year the book made its first public appearance. Francis soon found himself called upon for a second edition to which, at the request of the Bishop of Montpellier, he made notable additions. The second edition was a most phenomenal success! Translations were made into almost all European languages. Popes, cardinals, bishops and sovereigns adopted it for their daily use.

One critic called it "the most perfect and valuable book ever composed by mortal hand." Jane de Chantal exclaimed, "it is a book which the Spirit of God alone inspired." St. Vincent de Paul was so enchanted with the volume that he prescribed in the first rules for his Confraternities of Charity that a chapter of the book should be read every day.

The General of the Carthusians meeting Francis one day remarked naively, "Francis, never write again. You have achieved in this work the highest perfection, hereafter, you would produce nothing but what would be inferior."

Francis, fully appreciating the "involved compliment," laughingly retorted, "My dear Father Superior, if God has deigned to bless this little book, why should He not grant His blessing to a second?"

In a far different manner did Archbishop Pierre de Villars look upon Francis' success. "You must write again, since you have written so well," he urged. "I am delighted with your book which has done a signal service for religion and for souls. You, my dear friend, by striving to turn the wills of men from their passions, are attacking heresy at the root."

The story is told that Catherine de Medici sent a copy beautifully bound, with a decoration of diamonds and precious stones, to James I of England and that despite his prejudices, the English King conceived so great an admiration for the book that he always carried it with him and frequently read selections from it. One day he remarked in an annoyed tone to his son, Charles, "Why is it that none of our Bishops can write as beautiful, learned and practical a book as this that the Bishop of Geneva has managed to edit in the midst of his many activities?"

Upon another occasion he exclaimed, "How I should dearly love to know the author of this book. He is truly a remarkable man."

Later on, during the reign of his son, Charles, the book became so popular on the island and the Puritans were so incensed at its popularity and at the idea that Charles enjoyed the book almost as much as his father had, that they accused the King of leaning towards Catholicism and swaying the people in their reading matter. He, weak-kneed and selfish, decided to refute these comments by ordering all copies of the "Introduction" in the English kingdom to be seized and destroyed. Sixty years later, however, despite the proscription, "The Introduction" was once again in the hands of the Anglicans and Catholics across the English channel. Several centuries later one of the greatest converts from Anglicanism wrote of the book and its author, "Francis de Sales could not make of the narrow road a wide one—God forbid! But how many unnecessary briars has he not plucked out of it, how many a heavy stone has he not rolled aside from before our feet! Has he not made meditation more easy, prayer more confident . . . . . the world less dangerous and the love of God more practicable?"

Genuinely pleased with the unparalleled success of "The Introduction," Francis resolved to devote some of his precious time and energy to another book. The subject he selected was one dear to his heart, "The Love of God."

It is because of the collection of his singularly beautiful letters, because of his exquisite books and because of his founding the Florimonte Academy to stimulate the best in art, literature and science that Francis de Sales is often regarded as one of the Fathers of French literature, one worthy indeed to wear the laurel crown.

CHAPTER X

YELLOW AND PURPLE IRISES

T WO events which cast no foreshows occurred within the busy years of 1609-1610.

The first was an episcopal consecration. Surpassingly lovely were the seeds of the holy and intimate friendship that were sown that fair August morning in 1609 when Francis de Sales consecrated John Paul Camus as Bishop of Belley.

The genius and shining virtues of John Camus had attracted the attention of Henry IV who was ever eager to secure men of rare virtue and culture for his French bishoprics. It so happened that Father Camus was two years younger that the minimum age set by the Holy See for candidates to the episcopacy, but the King obtained a dispensation and the young priest was consecrated at the age of twenty-five.

Francis de Sales was delighted to discover in the young bishop a warmth of heart and a courtesy of manner that were akin to his own character. Too, he was attracted by Monsignor Camus' unique combination of zeal, fervor, piety, learning and wit, qualities that made him a most agreeable companion and a man of wide and generous sympathies.

In the Bishop of Geneva, John Paul Camus found a father, a friend and a saint. Francis' brilliant mind, his distinguished style of expression, his altogether delightful personality and his prudent counsel so charmed the younger man that he carefully noted and treasured every word and gesture until many years later they found expression in a most unusual biography which Bishop Camus wrote and published under the title, "The Spirit of St. Francis de Sales."

By a curious coincidence, the two dioceses adjoined, so it was arranged that each year the two Bishops were to spend a full week in each other's homes, "not counting the days of arrival and departure."

On one of the visits to Belley the discussion centered on the subject of preaching. "Long sermons are the most common fault of the orators of our days," remarked Francis with a judicious glance at John Paul who reveled in giving long, wordy orations.

The other Bishop was instantly alert. "Do you then," he challenged, "call that a fault, and call dearth what, in fact, is abundance?"

"When the farm," replied Francis, using one of his beautiful illustrations, "produces a great deal of wood, it bears the least fruit. A multitude of words does not always produce the greatest results. Read the homilies and sermons of the Fathers—how short! Yet how much more efficacious than ours! Good St. Francis of Assisi has prescribed by rule that the preachers of his order should be short. Believe me, I speak from experience, and from a long experience indeed. The more you say, the less they will carry away; the less you speak, the more they will profit."

"But," remonstrated the Bishop of Belley, "many are eager to hear the word of God and do not possess the necessary books which might supply them with spiritual food."

"My dear son," explained Francis kindly, "by overcharging the memory of the hearers, you will demolish it, just as a lamp is put out when we pour too much oil into it; and plants become generally rotten by watering them too much."

"What about those preachers who say the same thing over and over again?" asked John Paul, with a certain amount of complacency as he never repeated, even for emphasis.

"Again, I advise you to say little, but say it well and meet your point carefully. Care little for those who may find fault with you for repeating. Does not the painter lay his brush on the canvas many times before his work is completed? How much oftener, then, are eternal truths to be repeated in order that they may make an impression on hardened hearts?"

"I have never looked at sermons from this point of view," humbly acknowledged the enlightened Bishop of Belley.

"By the way," asked Francis, with a charming smile, "did I ever tell you about the learned orator, who took pains with his sermons, but was not favored with large audiences and consequently spent a goodly portion of his time in complaining of those who did not go to hear the Word of God?"

"No," answered the younger prelate, "you have never mentioned anything about him to me. Do tell me what happened to him."

"One evening," continued Francis, "as we were leaving the cathedral, after he had preached, a friend remarked to me 'against whom is that preacher angry? He has been scolding us for a fault of which were are not guilty. We were present. The absent will not improve as they did not hear him.' Imagine, John Paul, the poor deluded man spent his time in punishing the innocent instead of the guilty! Let us beware of doing likewise. As for myself, I can truly say I am always pleased when appearing in the pulpit to see few people, then the audience is like a clear coast before me."

"But it costs no more to teach many than a few," objected John Paul.

"My dear son," replied Francis, "I have invariably witnessed more good done in the service of God by those sermons I have preached before small audiences than before numerous ones. I will tell you an experience of many years ago. On a certain Sunday, the weather being very stormy, only seven persons were in church, and someone remarked that it was not worthwhile to preach. I replied that I felt neither encourged by a large audience, nor discouraged by a small one. Accordingly, I ascended the pulpit, and I remembered that my sermon was on the prayer of the saints. I handled my subject with great simplicity, yet one of my hearers began to weep bitterly, and even sobbed loudly. I thought something ailed him and interrupted my talk to beg the others to assist him."

"You must have been greatly distressed," encouraged John Paul.

"I was. I even told him that I would stop preaching for the evening and do all I could for him. He raised his eyes to me and pitiously begged me to continue, because I was dressing the very wound of his heart, he said. The sermon over; it was a very short one," Francis paused for a moment to glance at the Bishop of Belley, "the man threw himself at my feet and loudly cried, 'My father, you have given me life. This evening you have saved my soul. This hour is worth an eternity to me. For some time I have had conversations with some ministers who represented the prayer of the saints as horrible idolatry. They had so far, dear father, convinced me that it was so, that I had planned on this following Thursday, to abjure the Catholic church. Surely my dear, saintly mother has been praying for me and led me to the church tonight to hear you. I almost stayed at home, because of the terrible storm. Now, your sermon on the saints has cleared all my doubts. From this moment I renew my attachment to the Catholic church in which I was born and in which I shall die. Father, I beg of you, hear my confession and give me your blessing.' "

Francis' face glowed with happiness as he recalled the incident.

"What a signal grace for the poor man. How deeply the conversion must have impressed you!" exclaimed the interested Bishop.

"Yes, I was profoundly impressed, and I cannot

tell you what an impression the incident made in the country around. Many knew the gentleman and had heard his remarks about becoming a Huguenot. When the people heard that he recanted they became better disposed, and far more willing to listen to the word of God. Truly, the ways of God are admirable."

* * *

In late July, the Bishop of Belley spent his 'full' week at Annecy. Many delightful hours were lived in the glowing cathedral gardens, rich at this season with honey-yellow and deep purple irises. Here time flew on 'double wings' as the two friends exchanged confidences, exquisite joys and painful sorrows, that were doubled and halved by sharing with one another.

One bright, sunny morning as they watched the busy bees carefully choosing only the choicest flowers for their honey, the Bishop of Belley, turning to Francis with a serious expression, asked, "My lord, these busy bees remind me of souls who look for only the best in other people, while I am continually urging those who are guilty of looking for faults, real or imaginary, to amend their lives. What advice would you offer such busybodies who are frequently indulging in rash judgment?"

"My dear Bishop," exclaimed Francis, "all things look yellow to him who has the jaundice; now the sin of rash judgment is a spiritual jaundice which makes all things appear evil in the eyes of him who labors under it. Have your penitents drink deeply of the wine of charity which will clear them from their corrupt disease."

"A very fine comparison, my father," said the Bishop of Belley. "I always find rash judgments the greatest of all sins for people to eradicate. Sometimes I have fallen back on the remark often made that 'to detect faults, real or imaginary, is a much lower occupation than to recognize virtues.' "

"Suppose," suggested Francis, warming to his subject, "we approach the subject from another angle. Men see the exterior; God alone the interior. The soul of our neighbor is that tree of knowledge of good and evil which we are forbidden to touch under pain of severe chastisement, because God has reserved for Himself the judgment of each individual soul."

"Rest assured, my lord," replied John Paul, delighted with the answers, "that I shall make good use of your excellent suggestions."

"It is the sign of an idle mind to take delight in examining the lives of others," concluded Fran-

cis, "that thought ought to check the busy-bodies
if nothing else."

The following morning a storm of heat, with its
red-hot billows "beat like a sea" on the town of
Annecy. John Paul Camus, entering the Bishop's
room where the hot rays of the scorching sun were
heating every object they touched, exclaimed,
"what excessive heat! How can I ever endure it
the whole day?"

Francis, raising his head from a book he was
reading, asked quietly, "Wouldn't you like to have
a fire made?"

"What! Do you wish to finish broiling me?"
questioned John Paul.

"Did you not know that fire warms those who
feel cold, and cools those who feel warm?" Then,
after a pause, he added nâively, "you see, I was
playing double dealing; I remember having heard
you say that you dreaded the cold greatly, and
never felt too warm, and I wished to have a good
laugh at the excess heat you are suffering, and make
you remember what you have often said, that 'it
is better to sweat than to shiver."

The afternoon before John Paul left for Belley
the discussion centered on the subject of 'vocations.'
"Would," exclaimed John Paul, "that everyone
would take to heart the words of St. Paul, 'let

every man abide in the calling in which he is called.' Today, we see too many restless people, trying this calling then that profession."

"To be contented with one's vocation constitutes one of the sweetest pleasures in life," remarked Francis. "He who wishes for a change is never at rest."

The Bishop of Geneva looked quietly at his guest for a few minutes, then continued, "as you know, my son, for many years in the midst of my episcopal duties I have been faithfully praying for light and direction in regard to the religious community of nuns God has inspired me to found. Surely the time must be nearly ripe for the foundation. Now, my great aim is to train not one or two holy women up to great perfection, but to see that a number of such handmaids of God, as Spouses of the Lamb, are so prepared that from their midst at any time the Almightly may choose such as He sees worthy 'to abide in Him, to bury their lives in His Divinity, to live, in other words a life within a Life.' Do you grasp my idea?"

"No, I am afraid I do not!" answered the Bishop of Belley. "What do you really mean to do with this congregation of women and girls? Haven't we enough female orders to which they can attach themselves? Why waste your time with women to whom you must repeat things a hundred times before you are sure they understand?" demanded the young bishop who had little sympathy for women. "You," he resumed, "bury your treasure and place your light under the bushel! You paint on the waters and draw on the sand."

"It is not for me to work in such exalted undertakings: gold and silver for the goldsmith: clay for the potter," responded the humble bishop. "Believe me, God is a great workman. He does incomparable things with the poorest tools. By whose hands but a woman's did He conquer Holofernes? The weak sex has a great claim to compassion: thus we must bestow upon them greater care, even as the great St. Bernard says, 'the charge of souls regards the weak rather than the strong.' Our Divine Saviour did not deny His care to them. The church calls them 'the devout sex,' a token of no mean opinion, indeed! Too, take into consideration the good example they will give where ever God will place them. Is it of no account to spread the good odor of Jesus Christ?"

"As usual," laughingly rejoined John Paul, "you have over-ridden all my objections, by your powerful arguments. In my prayers, I shall be mindful of this new Order and beg God that your future nuns may be so virtuous that their 'good odor may, in pleasing God, be diffused in the hearts of the faithful.' "

The silver notes of the evening angelus shimmered in the clear, sweet air as the Bishop of Belley bade a fond adieu to his genial host.

"I shall appear in your diocese with the first snows of January," teasingly remarked the Bishop of Geneva. "Now, be sure to have a roaring fire for me, like the one I offered to have kindled for you the other day," he admonished playfully, a twinkle in his blue eyes.

* * *

The second event, as sad as the other was delightful, was the death of Madame de Boisy.

During late January and early February of 1610 Madame de Boisy's health, which had always been excellent, caused considerable anxiety to her children. She herself, feeling that death was near, went to Annecy to make a spiritual retreat and to prepare for death under the guidance of her son, Francis. Having devoted a month to this project she returned to Sales chateau where certain business matters awaited her attention. On Ash Wednesday she attended three Masses, received Holy Communion and assisted at Vespers in the parish church at Thorens. That night she was unable to sleep but insisted on rising the next morning and dressing for Mass. As she was finishing her toilet she was stricken with apoplexy and partially paralyzed. When Francis received the sad news of his mother's serious condition he at once, in company with a physician and apothecary, made his way to chateau Sales. Madame de Boisy, recognizing her son, took his hand and kissed it reverently, exclaiming, "I owe you this mark of respect, as my father."

Then, putting her arm around his neck, she drew his head down to her and gave him a motherly kiss on his lips, saying, "And as my son, I owe you this testimony of my tender affection."

Madame de Boisy then received Extreme Unction in a fully conscious state, and repeated lovingly the numerous acts of faith, hope and charity and contrition Francis suggested to her. She lived two and one half days after his arrival and gave her pure soul to God on the first of March. Francis gently closed her eyes, blessed her and gave her his farewell kiss. Then, he wept quietly at his great loss. Deeply bereaved, but fully resigned to the adorable Will of God, he presided over all of the last rites.

A short time later Francis returned to Annecy where in the month of April he was to receive the

Baroness de Chantal who was to talk over with him the foundation of the Visitation Order.

Chapter XI

WHITE VIOLETS

THE Easter alleluias were resounding in jubilant tones, and all creation joined in the grand chorus of praise in honor of the Risen Saviour when Francis de Sales summoned Madame de Chantal to Annecy for the promised interview. He felt that the time was now at hand for founding his religious Order and rejoiced that he had found a valiant woman who would walk nobly, courageously and fearlessly in the way commanded her. He foresaw that many fragrant flowers were to strew her path, but that they were "to rise behind her footsteps, not before them." Francis, determined, however, to make one final trial of the virtue of this unusual woman.

Seated comfortably in the 'Bishop-Prince Apartments,' as he loved to style his reception rooms, Francis turned to the Baroness and remarked, "I have made my decision, my dear daughter, in your regard."

"I am resolved to obey you in all things," answered Jane Frances with her winning smile.

"Well," said the holy Bishop, "I have decided that you are to become a Poor Clare."

"Your Lordship, I am quite ready."

"No," Francis hesitated, "you are not strong enough, you are to become an Augustinian nun."

"Father, anything you decide I shall abide by."

"That is not what I wish; you are to become a Carmelite."

"Even here, I am ready to obey you," replied Jane Frances gravely.

"No," Francis continued solemnly, "God does not want this of you. He has destined you to establish an Order in which the charity of meekness of Jesus Christ will reign."

"Your Lordship, if this is the will of God for me, I am resolved to obey."

From that moment Francis no longer hesitated in regard to the Baroness' fortitude of spirit in the pursuit of perfection. True, he foresaw innumerable difficulties that would arise, both for her and for himself, but all doubts about vocation were banished forever.

Madame de Chantal, in obedience to the Bishop of Geneva, now began her preparations for the new life slowly unfolding, day by day, and page by page, before her. Before she left Annecy she had obtained Francis' permission to tell her father

her intention to retire from the world. While she was visiting her father in Dijon during the latter part of June the opportunity, for which she had been awaiting, presented itself without any effort on her part.

It was St. John's Eve, a time sacred to old and young. In fact, the feast was so universal a favorite in France that many, many years before two rival armies coming face to face on June 23rd, by mutual consent, delayed their battle for another day. On this particularly lovely summer evening of St John's tide, when according to ancient custom St. John's fires were lighted on every hill and mountain top, and a special display of fireworks, new and startling, had been promised to the people of Dijon, all had left President Fremiot's home to see the marvelous illumination, (originated by the clever Chinese,) except Jane Frances and her father. Finding herself alone with him she began to discuss the education of her children.

"It is difficult, well-nigh impossible to bring up the children as well as I wish," remarked the Baroness.

"What is the trouble, my daughter?" questioned her interested father.

"Baron de Chantal's house is so badly kept that I find it a task to discipline the children as I should.

I tell them about wrong-doing, but when they see irregularities under their very eyes it isn't conducive to remedying evils."

"Do not trouble yourself about that," answered President Fremiot, "your eldest daughter is about to marry Francis de Sales' brother, the distinguished Baron de Thorens; the other two girls are old enough to be sent as boarders to a convent school; I myself will take charge of the education of Celse Benigne."

Jane Frances was delighted with her father's solution. Now, was the time to tell her plans.

"What an admirable arrangement," she exclaimed. "Please, dear father, do not be vexed with a proposal I am about to offer."

"What have you in mind? Would you like to live here in Dijon?"

"No, dear father. I should like to take advantage of this plan which you just suggested for educating my children, by leaving the world altogether and shutting myself up in a convent, where God has been calling me for a long time."

President Fremiot, utterly taken back at the idea, burst into tears. Moved by his distress, his daughter hastened to assure him that nothing had been settled but that she had consulted Francis de Sales upon the subject of her vocation, and that he felt certain that she was inspired by God in wishing to dedicate herself to His holy service.

"The Bishop of Geneva is inspired by the Spirit of God," acknowledged Monsieur Fremiot, "but, I beg of you to do nothing further until I speak to him about this matter."

"Dear father, I promise you that," she said.

The day after the wedding of Marie Aimee de Chantal and Bernard de Sales, Baron de Thorens, at Monthelon, Francis de Sales who had officiated at the ceremony held a consultation with President Fremiot and his son, the Archbishop of Bourges, in order to reach some decision in regard to Madame de Chantal's vocation. He told them that the idea of founding a new religious Order had not been formulated at a moment's notice but that for many years, both he and Madame de Chantal had been praying for light to know the Will of God. Now he felt that he would be acting contrary to Divine Providence if he opposed Jane Frances dedicating herself to God and he warned the President and the Archbishop to consider the matter well before they expressed their opinion. After fervent prayer and mature deliberation both father and son gave their consent with only one stipulation.

"My dear Bishop, my beloved daughter has my full consent, provided that the first house of your new Order be founded in Dijon," stated the President.

"No, my father, the first foundation should be made at Bourges where I can keep an eye on the little Institute," interrupted the Archbishop.

Jane Frances who had been summoned into their presence to hear their verdict glanced lovingly from father to brother and with a smile at the Bishop of Geneva said, "For two reasons it is absolutely necessary that the first Foundation be made at Annecy; in the beginning we shall need the founder's advice on many, many occasions, and secondly, living in the neighborhood of Thorens, I shall be able to help and train Marie Aimee in the management of her large household."

The President and the Archbishop submitted to the prudence of the reasons. It was definitely decided that Jane Frances should go to Annecy in about six weeks and that she should take her two smallest daughters with her to supervise their education. Celse Benigne was to stay with his grandfather, President Fremiot. There remained only the duty of making a last round of final farewells!

"Small clouds were sailing, blue skies were prevailing" and the spring rains were gone when, late in May, Jane de Chantal hastened to Monthelon,

the residence of the old Baron de Chantal. Here
she bade farewell to her father-in-law and her
numerous friends and acquaintances. Although the
surly old man had given little affection to his
lovable daughter-in-law, and had shown small appreciation for her many kindnesses to him, he was
loud in his outcries when she explained to him
what she was about to do. After some hours Jane
Frances was able to placate him and then she knelt
for his blessing.

Weeping copiously the old man said, "May you
have all the happiness you so fully deserve." He
then affectionately embraced her.

The farewells to the people of Monthelon, her
neighbors, servants, tenants and all the poor were
indeed nerve-racking. The Lady Bountiful of
the castle was to leave them; not for a few months,
but for all time.

"We are losing our all," they cried. "You have
been a refuge in need, a protectress in affliction and
a true mother to us at all times."

Displaying supernatural courage, the Baroness
said, "Good-bye forever, my vassals; good-bye, my
dear people, you will always be my children. I shall
pray for you. Fear God, and pray for me. Good-
bye all!" Then, mounting the waiting horses, she
and her attendants rode to Dijon where she must

bid a sad farewell to her father, President Fremiot, her little son, Celse Benigne, her daughter, Marie Aimee, and other relatives who with her two little daughters were awaiting her arrival in the Burgundian city.

What a scene of poignant tenderness occurred as Madame de Chantal said good-bye to the loving little group assembled at her father's house.

President Fremiot blessed his beloved daughter and exclaimed, "O, my God, it is not for me to call in question what Thy providence has set down in its eternal decrees. I acquiesce therein with all my heart, and with my own hands I sacrifice upon the altar of Thy Will this only daughter who is as dear to me as Isaac was to Thy servant Abraham." Then, kissing her fondly, he added, "Go then, my dear daughter, go where God calls you. I am confident that you will, by your prayers, support the old age of your father who permits your departure." Overcome with emotion, he then left the room, crying, "God keep you, my dear daughter."

Celse Benigne, who was only fifteen, and loved his mother passionately, flung himself on his knees and sobbed, "Dearest mother, renounce this rash purpose."

"My darling son, I cannot turn my back on God who is calling me!"

"Mother dear, do not leave us, please do not leave us," he pleaded.

In an agony of grief, but unshaken in resolution, his mother pressed her only son to her heart and explained to him once again, her reasons for leaving him. Celse Benigne remained unmoved.

Exhausted by the conflict, Madame de Chantal turned to leave the library. Celse Benigne, anticipating her movements, prostrated himself across the entrance and exclaimed, "Since I am unable to prevent you, my mother, it shall be said that you have trodden over the body of your own son!"

Jane Francis raised her tear-filled eyes to heaven in prayer, then, with a groan that pierced all hearts, and taking the hands of her two little girls, resolutely stepped over her son's prostrate body. For a few moments she quietly wept, then with a calm countenance turning to the group she said, "Pardon my weakness; I am leaving my father and son forever. But, faith consoles me, I shall find God everywhere."

The little group then set out for Annecy as Francis de Sales had selected the Pentecostal season for the beginning of his Order. It so happened, however, that the lady from whom he had hoped to secure a little home for his subjects, had changed her mind at the last minute so the opening of the

Gallery House was deferred until the Bishop signed the contract of possession in his own name. The sixth of June, the feast of St. Claude, and that year Trinity Sunday, marked the ceremony of the foundation of the new institute, to be first called "The Ladies of Mary," later to be known as "The Order of the Visitation of Our Lady."

* * *

Francis de Sales had two other ladies who had been eagerly awaiting the opening of The Gallery House, and the arrival of Madame de Chantal in Annecy. Mademoiselle de Brechard, a young noble lady of Nivernois, manifested so strong a desire to become a religious that the Bishop of Geneva, finding her the possessor of deep virtue and perfect charity, did not hesitate to pronounce that she was to be one of the foundation stones of the new order.

"Would you be willing to run, my dear child, with Madame de Chantal, for the same prize?" he had asked when telling her of his plans for the new institute.

"With the greatest pleasure, my Lord," she had answered with eagerness.

"Then pray fervently, my daughter, and wait. Strive daily to grow in the love of our good God for I feel that He wishes you to devote your life to His service in a new order," said the Bishop prophetically.

"I shall, your lordship, and in the meantime I shall continue to pick up the golden coins you told me about when I saw you last winter."

"Suppose you re-tell to me the story of the golden coins," gently suggested Francis, who was delighted with her mention of his challenge.

"I had been annoyed with my cousin who half-heartedly had helped me dust the reception room. I told you I was displeased with myself because I thought Catherine both careless and selfish in leaving me the greater part of the dusting. You said to me, 'Does a traveler who sees a gold coin lying by the roadside refrain from stooping to pick it up, saying to himself: why have not those who have covered the ground before me taken possession of it?' Then you explained to me that the piece of gold represents the work imperfectly done, or unfinished, which I should always hasten to make my own, upon discovery. You urged me, my lord, to follow the traveler's example and not to say a word about my find to anyone, fearful lest the treasure be taken from me."

"How beautifully you have remembered St. John Chrysostom's comparison which I told you months ago, my dear. Yes, by all means, take time and continue to gather the golden coins. Do so all your life and you will have sufficient funds to purchase a high place in the eternal mansions," urged Francis.

* * *

Then there was Madamoiselle Favre, the eldest daughter of the illustrious President Favre. Marie Jacqueline was most attractive, possessing a superior mind, good looks, agreeable manners and great conversational powers. She had many suitors and was in constant demand at all the balls as she was a most beautiful dancer.

"O, Mademoiselle Favre," had exclaimed poor Monsieur Chaillot, who had arrived quite late at the mid-winter ball at Chambery, "have you not one dance left for me this evening?"

"Not a half one," was the laughing retort, as Marie Jacqueline raised then quickly lowered her teasing, brown eyes.

"How can you treat me so unkindly," he woefully exclaimed. "You know I would rather waltz with you than with anyone else in the whole French kingdom."

"It is indeed, fortunate, Monsieur Chaillot, Mademoiselle Favre nâively remarked, "that no

ladies from the King's court are present tonight.
I have a feeling that Gabrielle d'Estrees, our king's
favorite, might take offence at your gallant words."

"Mademoiselle Favre, do not torture me! You
are beautiful, and you know it, but you are so
cold, so very cold-hearted!"

"I believe this is my dance, Mademoiselle Favre,"
remarked a handsome youth as he bowed low before the president's popular daughter who was
impatiently tapping her feet to the new waltz.
"Far be it from me," he continued, with a bow of
apology to Monsieur Chaillot for interrupting, "to
lose one diamond moment of the minuet with the
fairest and most exquisite dancer in Chambery."

"You flatter me, Baron de Mirabel," chided Marie
Jacqueline, "but come, we shall gather the diamond
moments that compose the golden hours. You
see, I too know the lines, 'lost two golden hours, each
set with sixty diamond moments,' " she quoted to
her amazed partner.

"Mademoiselle Favre, I am going to be very
honest with you; I have used those words about
losing the diamond minutes to each lady I have
danced with tonight and you are the only one who
had the wit, or the knowledge, to complete the
thought. You are indeed, unusual in every way.

I am charmed," he stated as he matched his steps to hers.

In the midst of the homage and adulation Mademoiselle Favre was obliged to retire to the powder room as someone had unluckily stepped on the train of her gown. As the maid was deftly stitching the tear Mademoiselle Favre had ample opportunity for reflection.

"Poor Marie Jacqueline," she said to herself, "of what avail will these measured steps which you take with such delight and such precision, be to you? People will say, 'How well Mademoiselle Favre dances' and that will be all. The glory of this world passes quickly. 'The longest memory of man is swift oblivion.' What a sad recompense." Convinced of the vanity of all worldly things she generously resolved to place herself under the direction of the saintly Bishop of Geneva, and if he thought she had a vocation, to leave the world.

Some weeks later, Louis de Sales asked President Favre for the hand of his eldest daughter. Delighted with the petition, the president hastened to inform his daughter. Here indeed, was a difficult situation for Marie Jacqueline. It was further complicated by the fact that the president was decidedly flattered by the proffered alliance. In her predicament Marie consulted the Bishop of Geneva, who had taken her under his spiritual direction after the mid-winter dance when she had petitioned his advice. Francis promised to untie the Gordian knot and strengthened her in her resolution to devote herself to God.

After a serious talk with President Favre, the holy bishop persuaded him that he was most fortunate, that his daughter had been favored by God with a religious vocation and that the father of a religious was indeed blessed.

With his brother, Louis, Francis used another approach. "Louis," announced Francis, as they were seated at the dinner table, "Do you know that you have a powerful rival?"

"What is this you are saying, my brother?" asked Louis, as he rested his fork on his plate.

"You have a rival to whom you will be obliged to yield your lady-love."

"Nonsense," shouted Louis, "Who would dare be a rival of mine for Mademoiselle Favre's hand?"

"It is a rival before whom brave as you are, you will tremble," replied Francis.

"I tremble before no man," excitedly boasted Louis.

"Your rival is Jesus Christ whom she has chosen for her Spouse, exclusive of any other. Therefore, I beg of you, Louis, to think no more about her."

"With God's grace," replied Louis with true Christian chivalry, "I will never oppose the vocation of Mademoiselle Favre."

Later in the week, in calling upon the young lady, with the Bishop, Louis, in extending his best wishes to her remarked, "Had you left me for another man I would be inconsolable, Mademoiselle, but for God I renounce my claims. I do not merit to be His rival."

* * *

As the early evening of June 6th melted into night, Madame de Chantal and her two companions Mademoiselle Brechard and Mademoiselle Favre left President Favre's home where they had been staying, and proceeded to the bishop's residence to ask his blessing. He, glowing with holy love, said to the three candidates whose faces were alight with spiritual joy, "You are indeed, most happy whom the Lord has chosen, my dear daughters. Keep your eyes lifted up to God. Have a great and humble courage. Augment this courage in holy humility, fortify it in sweetness. Never allow apprehensions to enter your hearts. Each day will give you the knowledge of what you shall best do the next. You have now entered upon a new state of life and by the grace of God have got over many a difficulty; the same grace will be present with you on all succeeding occasions, and will deliver you from obstacles, one after the other. Yes, though it were necessary for Him to send an Angel to help you over the most dangerous steps. Finally, let us have a firm and general purpose of intending to serve God with all our hearts, all of our lives. This done, let us not think of the morrow. Let us think only of achieving the present day well. We must make provision of manna for each day, and no more. God will rain manna tomorrow, and the day after tomorrow, and all the days of our earthly pilgrimage, provided we have a great confidence in His providence. Again, courage, my very dear daughters. God will be your God and you will walk victoriously over the head of your enemies."

Turning then to Jane de Chantal, Francis handed her an abridgment of the Constitutions of the Order. "Follow this road and teach all those whom Heaven has destined to walk in your footsteps to follow it," he enjoined.

Lastly, he raised his eyes to heaven and blessed the little band of pioneers, "in the name of the omnipotent God who is calling you, and in the name of the Son, the Eternal Wisdom who is directing you, and in the name of the Holy Ghost, who is vivifying you with the flames of His love."

How sweetly the little word-jewels of celestial melody fell on the love-attuned ears of the three kneeling women as the holy Bishop uttered his exquisite benediction!

On leaving the episcopal residence the three were escorted to the Gallery House by hosts of relatives, friends and well-wishers. After their cortege had departed and the women found themselves alone they went to the tiny chapel where, falling on their knees, they thanked God for His great and signal favors.

"Here, dear Sisters, is the place of our delight and our repose," exclaimed Jane Frances.

The Sisters then acknowledged Madame de Chantal as their superioress, and she, in turn, read them the rules drawn up and given them by their saintly Bishop. After evening prayer in common they retired, leaving as sentinels the fragrant bouquets of pure, white violets which loving hands had placed before the tabernacle. As the three exhausted Sisters slept, the perfumed flowers kept silent vigil with the hidden Christ.

Next morning, dressed in their religious habits, the Sisters assisted at their first community Mass, offered by Francis de Sales. After a brief exhortation on the fidelity with which they should observe the rules of their new state of life, the Bishop left on his numerous episcopal rounds. As he went from one duty to another his heart was warmed and gladdened by a picture of three brave, detached and generous souls who were living in the little Gallery House, laboring within the very shadow of the tabernacle where, day after day, the gleaming of their Spouse's love would brighten their abode and they would draw new strength and courage from 'the golden sunshine of the Blessed Sacrament.'

CHAPTER XII

AN ARMFUL OF MARGUERITES

SUCCESSIVE and successful months rolled past. Towards the last of July, Claude Roget and Peronne de Chastel, two ladies of eminent virtue, joined the little Visitandine band and in December Marie Milletot, Adrienne Fischet and Claude Marie Thiollier augmented the group so that they numbered eight. The desire uppermost in the mind of Mother de Chantal and her two first companions was to make their holy profession as soon as time would permit. After that they would feel definitely consecrated to God.

"When will that happy day arrive?" asked Mother de Chantal one afternoon, carried away with desire and enthusiasm for the happy event. She smiled as she thought of the happy occasion and continued, "Never before have I felt such a great desire of evangelical perfection."

Eventually the time of probation drew to an end. In 1611, on the 6th of June, a perfect day "when heaven tried earth" and found it in tune, Mother de Chantal and two of her spiritual daugh-

ters were professed by Francis de Sales who rejoiced with them in the course they were running.
What seraphic love filled the three holy souls as
they received their silver crosses, black veils and
crucifixes from the hands of their beloved Bishop
and Spiritual Father who admonished them that
thereafter they were to die to the world and themselves and live for God alone!

Overcome with emotion, Mother de Chantal
intoned the verse, "This is my Rest":

"Haec requies mea in saeculum saeculi.
    Hic habitabo, quoniam eligi eam."

Handing each Sister a wax candle, Francis spoke,
"Advance in the path of the just, like the resplen-
dent Aurora, and never cease to increase thy progress therein, until the perfection of day."

Several mornings later Francis sent a note to
Mother de Chantal and accompanied the note with
an armful of marguerites which his lackey had
gathered in the cathedral gardens. This missive
was dated June 10th, the Friday within the Octave
of Corpus Christi. The Bishop stated that the pre-
vious night he had been inspired to select a coat
of arms for his growing order which he felt was
now sufficiently established to merit such a distinction

"I thought, my dear Mother," he wrote, "that

if you agree with me, we will take as our arms a
heart, pierced by two arrows, enclosed with a crown
of thorns, this broken heart serving as a setting
to a cross, which will rise from it, and will be in-
scribed with the two names of Jesus and Mary.
The dying Saviour gave birth to us through the
wound of His Sacred Heart. Truly, my dear
mother, our little Order is the work of the hearts of
Jesus and Mary."

Many years later the significance of the
marguerites, and the note on the Sacred Heart
would bear abundant fruit in the efforts of Mar-
garet Mary of Paray le Monial, to spread devotion
to the same dear Sacred Heart. Providential indeed, were note and flowers that Friday of the
sweet, long ago!

As already a number of promising subjects had
joined the new Order and many more were begging
for admission, it behooved Francis de Sales to secure
larger quarters for his holy women. He was fortunate in buying the little maison de la Perriere for
additional quarters, and later in 1612 he added
still another house. In 1614 he purchased land surrounding the place bought in 1612, and on the 18th
of September of that year, he and his religious rejoiced to see the foundation stone of the First
Monastery of the Visitation laid by Baroness Claude

de la Croix who acted as proxy for the Duchess of Mantua who had joyfully accepted Francis' petition that she be patroness and protectress of the Visitation Order. Francis, having sung Mass before this ceremony, afterwards blessed the corner stone according to the usual custom.

That afternoon, returning to the convent for a short conference, the holy Bishop spoke on the beauty of poverty, calling it the most precious treasure of the children of God.

"For this reason, dear daughters, let us not seek temporal conveniences, on the contrary let us rejoice to be despoiled of the things of earth, since we participate in the riches of the house of God. True imitators of Jesus Christ love to see in their sacristies, dormitories, refectories and other places, the signs of holy poverty. Let us not use gildings and other similar ornaments, even in places destined to inspire devotion. If our devotion be true, we will be much more touched by modesty and simplicity than by all that would be ever so little connected with the luxury of the world."

Slowly but surely the new, red-brick walls, symbolic of the love burning in each Visitandine heart for her Spouse, rose heavenward. Many were the devout young women who sought for admission to the Order. Among them was Mademoiselle d'Ancre who was passionately loved by a young nobleman. Frustrated in his desire to marry the maiden, Baron Desolle imagined that Francis had urged Terese d'Ancre to enter the convent. Thoroughly angry, the nobleman hastened to the episcopal residence and unannounced, thrust himself into the Bishop's presence.

"By what authority have you placed Mademoiselle d'Ancre among your holy women?" he scornfully demanded.

"I did not place Mademoiselle d'Ancre in the convent," quietly answered Francis.

"Had you not advised her to leave the world and all its vanities, as you so call them," he remarked sarcastically, "she never would have refused my hand in marriage."

"My lord," said Francis, after he had listened calmly to the outcry, "be kind enough to examine the case impartially, you will find that I was not the adviser of Mademoiselle, but merely the approver of her choice."

Blinded by his passion the Baron shouted the louder, "I am sure she would have grown to love me, even as I love her, had you not maligned me and urged how superior the religious state is to that of marriage."

"Will you kindly lower your voice when insulting me," advised Francis, "I promise you, I will carry all your words to the foot of Jesus Crucified, and no one will know anything about this part of the interview where you calumniate me."

"I should like the whole world to know the little esteem I have for you."

"If my disgrace would redound to your credit I should like it too," approved Francis.

Enraged by the Bishop's suave manner, the Baron threatened, "This very night I will force open the doors of the convent, rescue Mademoiselle d'Ancre and burn down your fine monastery. I am sure many women will be happy to be released."

"My lord," meekly answered Francis, "you will do nothing of the kind. Almighty God will hinder your rash threats."

As soon as the menacing caller left, Francis sent word to the threatened convent that the young lady was to be lodged in the room farthest from the street, that lights were to burn in the convent all night and that all the Sisters should place their confidence in God.

True to his promise, the Baron and his retainers, from eleven until two, made themselves most obnoxious. Doors were knocked upon, stones and missals were hurled at the windows and a thousand insults were shouted to break the restful hours of sleep.

Early the next morning the bishop was informed of the nocturnal events. "Let us thank God," he exclaimed, " that it was nothing but a sound scattered by the wind. I already learned this morning that the young nobleman is now more provoked with Mademoiselle d'Ancre than with me. He thought she would at least put her head out of the window. Her silence which he thinks is due to contempt for him has so annoyed him that he swore that he will have nothing more to do with the haughty beauty."

In addition to settling little and great difficulties, which sometimes marred the calm for a few fleeting days, the Bishop, zealous and busy about his episcopal duties, managed to visit his spiritual daughters several times a week, and stimulated them in the pursuit of virtue by numerous little exhortations and conferences on the spiritual life.

What profound lessons he taught: love of God, perfect observance of religious duties, detachment from self, confidence in God, modesty of dress, of bearing, of language and of soul, and finally crowning all, the lowly, lovely virtue of humility. In order to animate his spiritual daughters to the practice of these virtues, he endeavored to impress their minds with little maxims, or adages, that he reiterated from visit to visit—"All things turn out well for those who love God," he was fond of stating, and—"All is vanity except eternity. Every day bring us nearer to this eternity and we already have one foot in it." Again, "We must suffer much for God before we enjoy Him."

On one occasion Francis spoke so fervently on the virtues of St. Joseph that the Sisters hastened to write down all the beautiful thoughts they could remember after the conference was ended. Thereafter they could frequently reread the golden eulogy on this great saint and pass the glowing words on to other admirers of Christ's foster-father.

"What a saint is the glorious St. Joseph," Francis had stated. "He is not only a patriarch, but the chief of all patriarchs; he is not simply a confessor, but more than a confessor; for in his confession is contained the dignity of bishops, the generosity of martyrs, and of all the other saints. And what a divine union between our Lady and the glorious St. Joseph! If the most holy Virgin was not only a virgin most pure and white but rather she was virginity itself: how great in this virtue must we suppose him to have been, who was chosen by the Eternal Father to be the guardian of her virginity, or rather to be the companion of it, since she did not need any other guard than herself? They both had made a vow to keep their virginity all their lives, and behold, God willed that they should be united by the bond of a holy marriage, not to make them revoke or repent of their vow, but that they might confirm and fortify each other to persevere in their holy intention; and therefore they vowed again to live together in virginity all the rest of their lives."

Then too," he had urged, "consider the beautiful humility St. Joseph exhibited. He is like the palm, prince of trees! The palm tree does not let its flowers be seen, till the vehement heat of the sun comes to burst the sheaths or cases in which they are enclosed, after which it suddenly shows its fruit. So does the just soul; it keeps its flowers, that is to say, its virtues, hidden under the veil of holy humility until death. How faithful in this respect was the great saint of whom we are speaking. It cannot be dwelt upon sufficiently. For, notwithstanding what he was, in what poverty and abjection did he not live all of his life! Under his poverty and abjection he concealed his great virtues and dignities. But what dignities! My God! to be the guardian of our Lord; and not only that, but to be also his reputed father. To be the husband of His most holy mother! Oh, I have indeed no doubt that the Angels, ravished with admiration, came in troops to contemplate him and to admire his humility when he kept that dear Child in his poor workshop, where he labored at his trade to support both the Son and the Mother who were confided to him.

"There is no doubt, my dear Sisters, that St. Joseph was more valiant than David, and wiser than Solomon; yet who could have thought so, without being enlightened by heavenly light, seeing him reduced to exercise the trade of a carpenter? So completely did he keep hidden all the signal gifts that God had bestowed upon him. But, what amount of wisdom did he not possess, since God gave him in charge, His most glorious Son, and chose him to be His guardian?

"The palm has a strength and a valour, and even a great constancy, beyond all other trees. It shows its strength and constancy in that the more it is burdened, the more it rises and the taller it grows; it shows its valour by its leaves being in the form of swords, and it seems to have as many weapons to fight with as it has leaves. It is certainly with good reason that St. Joseph is said to resemble the palm-tree for he was always very valiant, constant, and persevering.

"Now who can doubt that this wonderful saint

has great credit in heaven with Him who has so favored him as to raise him to it in both body and soul; which is the more probable as we have no relic of him here below on earth; and it seems to me that no one can doubt this truth. For how could He who had been obedient to him all His life, have refused this grace to St. Joseph? No doubt, when our Lord descended to Limbo, St. Joseph spoke to Him in this manner: 'O my Lord, I pray Thee to remember that when Thou camest to earth from heaven, I received Thee into my house, into my family; and that as soon as Thou wast born, I received Thee into my arms; now that Thou art going to heaven take me with Thee. I received Thee into my family, receive me now into Thine. I have carried Thee in my arms, now carry me in Thine; and as I took care to support and guide Thee during the course of Thy mortal life, do Thou take care of me and guide me to life eternal.'

"Oh, how happy should we be, if we could deserve to have a share in his holy intercession! For nothing will be refused him, either by our Lady or by her glorious Son. He will obtain for us, if we have confidence in him, a holy growth in all virtues, virtues which will render us victorious over our enemies in this life, and make us merit the grace to enjoy in eternal life the reward promised and prepared for those who shall imitate the example given by St. Joseph, a reward which will be nothing less than eternal happiness, in which we shall enjoy the clear vision of the Father, of the Son, and of the Holy Ghost."

And thus the days of the Visitandines passed, most of them in peaceful serenity, as the Sisters went silently and happily from work to prayer to work. Among their daily duties was the obligation of visiting the sick and needy, an activity Francis de Sales was particularly insistent upon as he wished his daughters to combine the active life of Martha with the contemplative life of Mary. In the early 17th century it was an unusual sight to see Religious going about the street, administering to spiritual and corporal needs. In fact, many thinly-veiled and contemptuous remarks were made by even the well-meaning who could not become quite reconciled to the founder's unique idea. Nevertheless, Mother de Chantal and her obedient daughters braved public opinion and zealously followed in the footsteps of their Master, going about doing good.

Early in 1615, Cardinal de Marquemont, Archbishop of Lyons, persuaded Francis to establish a monastery of the Visitation in his city. On the 26th of January he dispatched the new colony under the temporary charge of Mother de Chantal. No sooner were the Sisters settled in their abode in the rue Griffon than they began to prepare for their daily tasks of caring for the sick and visiting the poor and needy. To the amazement and consternation of Mother de Chantal the Archbishop firmly forbade the Sisters to go into the streets.

"If you wish to go about in the world then you should remain in the world," exclaimed the old-fashioned bishop who hated innovations. "Since you have taken the veil you must remain within the monastery walls like other women consecrated to God. Do you see the Carmelites and Poor Clares wandering about the streets and highways? I shall write to the Bishop of Geneva that I firmly believe that the solid establishment of this new Order of his demands the enforcement of enclosure and the obligation of solemn vows."

True to his word, Francis very shortly received a letter from the Archbishop of Lyons petitioning him to change his original plans for the Order of the Visitation. Actuated by no other desire than the glory of God, Francis, though he did not wish his Sisters to be subjected to enclosure, consented to the proposed change. Several months later he wrote to one of the Sisters at Lyons:

"I am quite indifferent as long as good is done.

I agree, then that we make our Congregation a formal religious Order, and I speak to you with simplicity and confidence. In all this I aim only at the greater honor and glory of God, and that He may be better known and loved by those who dedicate themselves to His holy service.

"Rest assured, my daughter, that I truly love our little congregation, but without anxiety. God's sovereign Hand can do more for our Institute than men can think."

Thus the little Congregation was converted into a religious Order with strict enclosure. In April of 1618, Francis de Sales received from Pope Paul V a Bull authorizing him to form into a religious Order, under the Rule of St. Augustine, the Institute of the Visitation.

It was about this time that Francis humbly and wittily remarked, "I am called the founder of the Visitation. Yet, I ask you, what is more unreasonable? I have done what I did not wish to do, and I have undone what I wished to do."

Chapter XIII

ANGELS' FORGET-ME-NOTS

Francis found
"Time to work as well as pray
Clearing thorny wrongs away;
Plucking up the weeds of sin,
Letting heaven's warm sunshine in."

DURING the busy years that followed the foundation of the first monastery of the Visitation, and the early foundations in several other French cities, it is amazing to note the vast amount of work that the good Bishop of Geneva accomplished in his diocese and in the whole Duchy of Savoy. True, he gave his money to the poor but in addition, he gave his time, his heart, himself, sparing nothing in the service of God and of souls. Never did he refuse to interview a caller, no matter what day nor hour he was summoned. And each visitor, either spiritually or materially the richer, left the gracious prelate with fervent joy and praise.

It sometimes happened that apostates would appeal to the Bishop of Geneva for refuge. He regarded them as his dear lost children and opened wide arms and heart to them. One day a visiting religious was scandalized to hear him warmly welcome a well-known apostate.

"Come, my child, come into my arms," exclaimed Francis as he joyfully greeted his guest. "God will assist you and I will be His instrument. Do not yield to despair: with our Lord's help everything will be all right again."

"My lord," admonished the religious after the sinner had left, "you seem to be eulogizing wickedness and are allowing it to go unpunished. Rest assured this act will be followed by bad consequences."

"Ah," answered Francis with a gentle sigh, "are these people not my sheep? My Saviour gave them all of His blood: how could I refuse that poor man my tears? They whom you look upon as wolves will become lambs, by degrees: nay, the day will come when they will become greater saints than any of us."

"Greater than any of us!" repeated the visitor in indignation.

"Had Saul been rejected, we never would have had Paul. Have a little patience and charity, my friend. Tell me, I pray, to whom ought we to be merciful, if not to sinners? God sends them to me so that I may heal them and draw them from the abyss of perdition. Would you have me thwart the designs of God? As their Bishop I know it is my duty to admonish them somewhat severely; but I prefer to treat them with the tenderness of paternal love. He who is in favor of severity need not expect a hearing from me: I will not enlist in his party, for it is my firm resolution not to be severe."

"I do believe your lordship would make excuses for even our so-called 'reformers,' " challenged the priest.

"Do not condemn them," advised Francis. "Our conjectures might be wrong. The grace of final perseverance does not depend upon merit. The secret to whom it shall be given God reserves to Himself.

"Who knows but at the hour of his death God touched Luther's heart by His efficacious grace? It is true that if he is not damned he has had as narrow an escape as any man ever did, and no one could ever have a greater debt of gratitude to God than he; but we must have unbonded confidence in the goodness of God for He is infinitely rich in mercy towards those who call upon Him. Did not Jesus offer His peace, His love and salvation to His treacherous disciple? Why could He not have offered the same grace to Luther and other unfortunate heresiarchs?"

Whenever Francis conversed with people of distinction he showed them the greatest honor, always addressing them by the title he thought most pleasing to them. Here too, some of his friends thought him to be at fault.

"Look at those two men from the country," complained a visiting Bishop to Francis, "they are as poor as Job and yet put on airs like princes and lords. Moreover, they incessantly boast of their nobility, and the great deeds of their ancestors."

"And why?" Francis asked glancing down the street at his two departing callers, "would you want these poor people to be doubly poor? They console themselves in their poverty by thinking themselves rich in honor; this is a weakness we must put up with."

One bitterly cold day, Francis saw a shabbily clad man, shivering with hunger and cold, enter the room. Filled with compassion, the kind Bishop excused himself for a moment and returned with a bowl of steaming broth and warm rolls.

"Enjoy this nourishing food while I attend to a little matter of business," he said in his most winning manner.

Leaving the old man before the glowing fireplace, enjoying the unlooked for luxury of hot food, the thoughtful Bishop went to his wardrobe to secure some warm clothing. Finding nothing, he removed the coat he was wearing under his cassock, and gave it to the pauper.

Another day it was a nobleman from Normandy, who was troubled with scruples and doubts against faith. Having found no relief in Normandy, nor in Paris, he remembered the fame of the holy Bishop of Geneva and hastened to Annecy to the episcopal residence to ask for help. When he arrived, the Bishop and his household were at dinner. When Francis heard that a traveler wished to speak with him he immediately arose from the table, though he had only started his dinner, and took the stranger to his room.

The nobleman at once began to explain his doubts and difficulties to Francis. Hour after hour flew by. As soon as one problem was laid to rest, another loomed in its place. Suppertime came around. Someone went to summon Francis. The others waited some minutes then, when he failed to make his appearance, they proceeded to eat the already cooling meal. Another hour passed. A priest knocked at Francis' door and whispered to the Bishop who seemed oblivious of time and place,

"Unless you eat some food, my lord, you are likely to weaken yourself seriously. Too, you will be overcome by fatigue."

"Is not life more than food?" he asked. "My meat at all times is to do the will of my Father. We shall have time for eating and drinking later on. Let no one come and disturb me again."

More hours elapsed, until all doubts and difficulties being vanquished the happy nobleman took his leave. Turning at the door to the Bshop's lackey the departing visitor said, "I bless God for bringing me to your holy Bishop. I had heard many wonderful things about him; yet all that I heard was but a shadow of what I have seen."

The conference between Francis and the nobleman had lasted ten hours!

Not only were scruples vanquished and souls restored to grace, but often sick persons were healed by the good Bishop's prayers and saintly touch. One day some very sick people were taken to the episcopal residence by friends.

M. Rolland, ever faithful and devoted to Francis approached him and begged, "My lord, cure them."

"I am delighted," said the Bishop smiling, "that M. Rolland teaches me how to work miracles."

Francis then prayed over the afflicted and gave

them his blessing. Fully restored by the prayers and episcopal blessing the sick persons left the Bishop's home in joy and thanksgiving.

One Sunday afternoon Francis took for his sermon the text from St. Matthew, "If any man strike thee on thy right cheek, turn to him the other also." As he was leaving the cathedral in company with several friends who were delighted with the Bishop's interpretation of the Evangelist's remarks a Calvinist publicly accosted him in a very rude manner.

"Since you tell us that when one cheek is struck, the other should be presented, that is doubtless the cause of both of yours being red," he tauntingly remarked with a sneer.

Francis, and his companions, looked in amazement at the accoster.

"Tell me," continued the insulting stranger, "if I were now to give you a box, would you really practice what you have been preaching and teaching? It is more probable that you are of the number of those who say and do not."

"My friend," replied Francis gently, "I know very well what I ought to do, but I do not know what I might do, for I am a miserable creature. I put my trust in the grace of God, Who can turn a frail reed into a firm pillar. But if, proving un-

[187]

faithful to grace, I should not happen to bear the insult in a Christian manner, then my words and not my works are to be followed."

"But," objected the Calvinist, "our Saviour did not offer His other cheek to the servant of the high-priest, when he was struck by him."

"Would you then reckon our Saviour among those who do not observe what they teach?" asked Francis. "God preserve us from thinking thus of Him Who is the model of perfection," he said reverently. "All His works are perfect, and we have no right to blame any of them. Nevertheless, it is easy to imagine the reason why our Lord did not offer His other cheek. Burning with zeal for the salvation of that impious man, He wished to move him to repentance, by drawing his attention to his fault. Later on in His Passion, He practised most perfectly the counsel which He had given; for He presented not only His cheek but His whole face, to the blows and spittle of the rabble, and His entire body to the scouragers."

The Calvinist, satisfied with this answer, left. Francis' friends, indignant that the Bishop did not rebuke the bold young man for his insolence, chided him for his mildness.

Every Monday and Thursday Francis stood at the door of his home and distributed general alms to the poor. Bread, pottage, vegetables and clothes were given according to the individual's needs. Sometimes, if he had no money on hand he would borrow rather than send the indigent away. On one occasion a parishoner approached him and asked for a loan of twenty crowns. Francis managed to get half the sum requested together and said to the borrower, "I have found a way which will mean gain for both of us if you will take my advice."

"What must I do?" questioned the man who was not adverse to turning over a little profit.

"There is nothing easier," answered Francis, "we have nothing to do but open our hands, you and I. Now, here are ten crowns, which I am offering to you as a gift instead of lending to you twenty; you will therefore gain these ten which I give you, and I will consider myself as gaining the other ten if you relieve me of the obligation of lending them to you."

"What an excellent expedient, my Lord," exclaimed the delighted man who went away extolling the wisdom and generosity of the holy prelate.

Not always, however, was Francis so successful in pleasing beggars. One morning when Francis was busy writing his book "The Love of God," a pauper covered with rags presented himself at the episcopal residence. Francis, after hearing of his needs, told his servant to give the man one of his garments.

"Your lordship, see what he is giving me," wailed the crusty old man. "See, it is patched."

"See if there is not a better one there," said Francis kindly to his valet.

"No, my lord, that is the best of all you have," he said after examining all the Bishop's apparel.

"Alas, my friend," said Francis to the arrogant old beggar, "I have nothing better than this, be so good as to be satisfied with it."

Monsieur Deage, Francis' old preceptor, was often chagrined at the number of women who went in crowds to consult their Bishop. When he knew that Francis was engaged in writing his new book he took the liberty permitted him by his old pupil of remonstrating with him at the facility with which he made himself available to all people at all times.

"Where is your charity, M. Deage?" he asked kindly. These people are my neighbors. No matter what the hour may be, I shall not refuse to see anyone."

"But, this crowding of women to you is out of place," urged M. Deage, "and I fear that wicked tongues will make use of it to assail your reputation, which I hold dearer than my own."

"Monsieur," said Francis, "God Who is charity, has placed me in a position of charity, where I am indebted to all, especially to the weak and infirm. Our Lord knows that in all this I have only His love in view."

"But you do not say much to them so why let them take up your time?"

"Ah, you call it nothing to let them have their say! They have more need of someone with ears to hear them than with a tongue to speak to them. They say enough for themselves and for me."

With a teasing glance at his old teacher he concluded, "It is probably this facility of being heard that causes them to come to me; for nothing pleases a good talker more than a patient listener."

"Your lordship," continued M. Deage, who was determined not to finish the conversation unsatisfied, "look at Bishop Laurenti, as you know, he will not allow women no matter of what condition of life, to enter his palace. He defends himself by the example set by the great St. Augustine. I have been told that he had grates built in a chapel and that is the parlor where he receives persons of of the opposite sex."

Francis, who was very partial to the prelate in

question, would not pass any censure on the arrangement. He only smiled and playfully remarked, "Bishop Laurenti is only half a Bishop since he has separated himself from half his flock."

About this time Francis was subjected to a violent attack of hatred. Monsieur Pellet, a lawyer of Geneva, had conceived an intense dislike for the holy Bishop. In fact, he seized every opportunity to heap upon him all kinds of injury and calumny. At first, Francis tried to appear unaware of the persecution, and maintained a charitable silence.

One day, meeting the calumniator face to face, Francis accosted him kindly, "You wish evil to me, my friend, nevertheless, if you pluck out one of my eyes, I will not cease to look lovingly at you with the other."

This excess of goodness did not disarm Monsieur Pellet who even went so far as to fire pistols at Francis during the Corpus Christi procession when he was carrying the Blessed Sacrament. Seeing that the Bishop was unharmed Monsieur fired pistols at the episcopal windows the whole of the following night. A strange and novel practice for a famous lawyer.

When Louis de Sales heard how Francis had born these insults and calumnies without uttering a word he asked, "Have you felt no movement of anger?"

"Certainly, I did," answered Francis. "My blood was boiling in my veins like water in a vessel on the fire, but by dint of careful examination of conscience, which I have constantly practised for twenty-two years, and with the help of unwearying watchfulness, constant struggles and repeated victories, I have, if I may be allowed the expression, so collared my anger, that it is now within my power."

One morning a very disturbed woman presented herself at the chancery office and demanded to see the Bishop of Geneva immediately. Francis, who was in the adjoining room and heard her request stepped into the office and asked, "What can I do for you, my dear Madame?"

"When my husband was well he left me and went to help Louis and his wars, now he has come home sick and wounded, cross and peevish, and wants to be nursed," she complained bitterly.

"Well," asked Francis tolerantly, "in what sauce would you cook? He cannot stay with you when he is well, and you cannot, seemingly, stay with him when he is sick. If you loved each other in God you would not be subject to these feelings; your affection would always be the same, whether present or absent, sick or well. Fervently beg this gift of God; for unless you have it I despair of your ever having any rest."

In his guidance of others Francis always recommended the virtue of meekness. "The human heart is so constituted," he remarked one day to Georges Rolland, "that it rebels at rigor. Harshness spoils everything. It exasperates the heart and engenders hatred. Kindness, on the contrary, leads the heart of man as it pleases and shapes it according to its designs. Remember that to prepare the salad well you need more oil than vinegar. If you must go to extremes, M. Rolland, let it always be the extreme of kindness."

On a certain evening one of Francis' servants who was fond of liquor, and had received several reprimands for over-indulging, went out to satisfy his thirst and forgot to return until very late at night. No one was awake to answer the poor domestic's summons except Francis who found him so intoxicated that he had to take him by the arm, lead him into the house, up to his room, remove his clothes and put him to bed. The following day the servant dreaded to meet the Bishop.

When Francis met him alone he merely said, "My dear friend, you were very sick last night."

At these words the poor man went down on his knees and asked the Bishop's pardon. Francis, touched by his contrition, paternally admonished him and the servant never again went to excess in drinking.

Another time, Francis' kindliness and humility under unjust persecution melted the hardened heart of Monsieur Bererd who though scarcely acquainted with the Bishop of Geneva hated him intensely. Monsieur prided himself on being a popular wit and first attacked Francis by spreading bitter satire against him. Seeing that the Bishop remained undaunted and that even the people of Annecy paid no attention to the tale, the nobleman resorted to a cruder and more stupid form of annoyance. One cold January night he staged a hunting party on the episcopal grounds. He assembled his retainers, ruffians—gathered hither and yon— dogs and hunting horns outside the Bishop's bedroom windows. What an infernal noise they all made as the horns were blown, pistols were fired, dogs were forced to howl and bay and the vagabonds shouted all kinds of taunts throughout the hours Francis tried to sleep. Finally, finding sleep impossible, the scoundrels had "murdered sleep" for the entire neighborhood, the Bishop rose and spent the remaining time in prayer for his tormentors, repeating slowly and carefully the words of the Our Father. The court-yard entertainment was re-enacted for several nights. Utterly exhausted, the Bishop's household wanted to disperse the band with armed forces.

Francis remonstrated kindly, "Do nothing of the sort. They are more to be pitied than we are. Consider, we are warmly housed and clothed, they, poor deluded creatures, must be shivering with the winter cold."

"But, your lordship," pleaded M. Rolland, "we need our rest. It is impossible to do one's best when the body is greatly fatigued."

"Have recourse to prayer," suggested Francis. "All difficulties can be solved by this method alone. It has been beautifully said that 'prayer is the for-get-me-not of God's angels.' Let us make use of this little blue-blossomed flower."

Matters, however, went from bad to worse until Francis happened to meet Monsieur Bererd, the prime cause of the nocturnal disturbances. Before the nobleman had an opportunity of addressing him, Francis greeted him as if he were his best friend and cordially embraced him. Utterly unprepared for such condescension, Monsieur Bererd completely surrendered to the Bishop's charm and begged his pardon for all the unpleasantness.

Several months later, after Monsieur had entirely reformed his life and had become an admirer and disciple of Francis he was heard to remark, "The charity of the Bishop of Geneva has exercised more power over my soul than the sermons of a hundred other preachers."

During the month of December, when all good people were preparing for their Saviour's advent, a most bitter and violent quarrel occurred between Monsieur Bererd's brother, Jacques, and the Marquis Cergues, a wealthy and illustrious lord. The cause of dispute had been trivial, a mere matter of preference for two different French artists, but, day by day, the disagreement grew, insult was added to insult, until, accordingly to public opinion, matters could not be settled until the two adversaries resorted to a duel.

The Marquis Cergues accepted Jacques Bererd's challenge, and journeyed to Annecy accompanied by twelve horsemen. As he passed down the rue St. Claire he glanced at the episcopal palace where he had frequently visited. The Bishop of Geneva was standing at his door and motioned to the nobleman that he wished him to dismount and talk to him.

"My dear son," said Francis as he greeted his guest and led him into the house, "this is the holy season of peace. Let thoughts of the Christ Child's heavenly gift which He came on earth to proclaim find lodging in your heart and dismiss all ideas of fighting and contention. An ounce of peace is better than a hundred pounds of wealth and of vain honor."

The Marquis was struck with wonder at these words of the holy Bishop as he himself had told no one of his intention of duelling.

"My lord," said the Marquis gently and thoughtfully, "would that I possessed some of your imperturbable peace!"

"Even though the universe were turned upside down," said Francis soothingly, "there is really no need of being troubled because even the whole universe is not worth the peace of the soul. Think, my very dear son, what a trivial matter has caused you and your friend to become so angry."

The Marquis Cergues, touched by Francis' kindly admonitions, resolved to make peace with his antagonist and asked Francis to act as his arbitrator in the matter. The Bishop did, so charitably and prudently that in a very few days the two former friends were completely reconciled, warmly embraced one another, and again renewed their pledge of friendship which was never thereafter broken.

Chapter XIV

THE PERFUME OF LILIES

THE versatile labors and marked genius of Francis' never grew old—"they were young today, mature yesterday, vigorous tomorrow, always eternal."

Francis imitated the busy bees in his many duties and activities. He no more than finished one occupation than another awaited his attention. In all his multiplicity of works, however, he made 'haste slowly' and kept his soul in a state of utmost quiet and repose. He was never, never agitated by his many calls and labors. Indeed, after lovingly accepting each project for the greater glory of God he calmly abandoned the outcome to Divine Providence.

During the spring and summer of 1616, a considerable part of Savoy was suffering from famine due to an unusual drought. Corn was scarce and hungry mouths were numerous. Fortunately, Francis was able to arrange for a distribution of small supplies of grain twice a week to all who begged, and for those who were ashamed to ask

[199]

for food he managed that sustenance be given secretly.

The epidemic of famine was followed by the horror of Civil War. In May, the Duke of Nemours and Geneva rebelled against his ruler in Savoy. An army of 800 men, speedily raised in Geneva and Faucigny, took their position near La Plot, between Annecy and La Roche. When the Governor of Savoy learned of this he immediately occupied the suburbs of Annecy and won to his side the commander of the Duke of Nemours' troops, at La Plot. Moreover, he sent Francis' brother, Louis de Sales, to surround and disarm the soldiers. All was successfully accomplished. About a month later, however, another follower of the Duke of Nemours, Colonel la Grange, journeyed to Annecy with three companies of French auxiliaries. On the 22nd of July the colonel presented himself at the gate of the city and demanded entrance. He was refused. He then threatened to take Annecy by force. Panic spread among the people.

Francis, in order to allay their fears, spoke to his parishioners from the pulpit the following Sunday, saying in part, "Place your unbounded confidence in God. Then, rest assured that these military operations will be of short duration. Providence may delay assistance for a short time, but it will be only to try our confidence; to keep us near to Him and to give us an opportunity to urge Him with loving violence as did the disciples at Emmaus. I can promise you, my dear people, that these great princes will soon come to a satisfactory agreement."

In the meantime Francis friends were most anxious for his safety. After talking the matter over among themselves they approached him.

"If the enemy should succeed in taking Annecy you will be the first object of their attack as many of those French auxiliaries are Huguenots," explained Monsieur la Comte.

"I do not think that the enemy have any greater grudge against me than against the rest of our people. As a watchful shepherd, I must and shall remain with my flock," answered Francis calmly.

"At least, my lord, common prudence suggests that you pack your valuables and send them outside the city," urged Monsieur Benoit, another close friend.

"If there are dispatches to write and to send out of the city, I shall do so, but I have no wealth to store away. With the help of God I shall continue to perform my regular duties and if the enemy take the city and intend to harm me, well, here I am in the hands of Divine Providence."

The Bishop's and his people's trust in God was rewarded. In a few days, Colonel le Grange, learning that the citizens were prepared to defend Annecy, and that the Governor of Savoy with an armed force was advancing, withdrew from the city.

On the 12th of August, Victor Amadeus, Prince of Savoy, and son of the Duke, arrived in Annecy to re-establish order in Geneva and to negotiate with the Duke of Nemours. The Prince went directly to the Bishop's palace, where he conferred with Francis and his brothers and spent the night. This was the Bishop of Geneva's first meeting with Victor Amadeus and he was so delighted with the excellent young man that he later wrote to a friend:

"He is the most kind, gracious, and religious Prince that could be met with; a heart full of courage and justice, a mind full of discernment and intelligence, a soul which is given up entirely to goodness and virtue, the love of his people, and above all the fear of God."

On August the 13th, Victor Amadeus took formal possession of the Duke of Nemour's palace and order was soon reigning in the Duchy.

In the midst of all the storm and stress of sickness, famine and Civil War, Francis completed and published his greatest work, "The Love of God." In the preface of this treatise, the Bishop wrote:

"I do not pretend to be an author; I have not the brilliancy of imagination requisite for such a profession; nor is my station in life, which of itself consecrates all my faculties to the good of souls, and obliges me to give assistance to all who claim it, compatible to the avocations of a public writer. With respect to the plan I pursue in the composition of my works, I may compare myself to a lapidary, who, when his sight becomes fatigued, from protracted efforts to impress a line on the surface of a diamond, turns his eyes on a bright emerald, and, relieved by its grateful hue, is soon enabled to resume his labors. Thus amid the multitude and variety of the weighty duties attached to my ministry, I console myself with the project of some pious book, to which I direct my exertions, when allowed by my more important avocations.

"It is said that Phidias excelled in statues of the gods, and Apelles in representations of Alexander. I should be glad were the same observation applicable to me on the subject of the love of God; but our efforts are not always attended with success.

"Before the birth of their children, mothers choose God-parents from among their worldly friends, but afterwards, when pain and exhaustion

have reduced them to the last extremity, they recur
to the aid of the saints, and engage themselves by
vow, to select a sponsor, either a poor person, or
one remarkable of piety, in the name and to the
honor of St. Joseph, St. Francis of Assisi, St.
Nicholas, or some other citizen of heaven, in order
to obtain, through his intercession, their own safe
delivery and the delivery of their offspring. Thus
before the weighty duties of the episcopacy had
devolved on me, I dedicated my works to the mon-
archs of the earth; but now that I am overpowered
by the obligations of my ministry, I address the
productions of my pen to the Princes of the
heavenly court, trusting that they will procure me
the assistance I stand in need of, and obtain that,
if the Lord deign to use me for His glory, my
writings may be favorably received by the public,
and tend to the advantage of many souls."

No sooner was the treatise, twelve books, bound
in one, in the hands of the public than it was
widely acclaimed. The Jesuits declared that by
this great work Francis had placed himself on a
level with the great doctors of the church and the
General of the Carthusians, who had declared after
reading "The Devout Life" that the holy author
should write no more lest he run the risk of not
maintaining his high standard, now sent him a

letter begging him never to cease writing again in the future.

James I, who had so greatly esteemed "The Devout Life" was so carried after perusing the "The Love of God," that he cried out to his son, "If only once I might see the author of this heavenly book. His language is celestial, not terrestrial. He must be a very great saint."

When Francis learned of these words of James' he exclaimed, "Would that I had the wings of a dove, that I might fly to the King of the fair island, once the island of saints, now the abode of heresy."

In fact, Francis requested that he might go to England for a few months, but Charles Emmanuel would not permit his going. Too valuable indeed was the Bishop of Geneva in Annecy!

During the Pentecostal season of 1617 Francis worked several miracles which aroused the ire of the Huguenot ministers who had been duly alarmed at the Bishop's successful series of Lenten sermons preached in Grenoble.

As a result of a severe fever, one of the diocesan priests became quite mad. In a few days he was so violent and dangerous that his friends were obliged to keep him chained in prison. On several occasions, however, the poor crazed man escaped from his bonds and at one time made his way to

Annecy where his arrival caused great consternation among the populace. In order to calm the frightened people, Francis ordered that the priest be incarcerated in the episcopal prison. A few days later he visited the cell where Cure de la Chenal was confined and spoke to him.

"Cure de la Chenal, come here," Francis said kindly.

The patient quietly obeyed the summons and allowed the Bishop to stroke his hair and cheek. After a few gentle words and a blessing, Francis bade the poor priest to thank God for curing him. He then left the prison and gave orders for the priest's release.

"Your lordship," entreated Monsieur Rolland, "It will be dangerous to have this poor man at large."

"M. Rolland, do as I tell you. Moreover, Cure de la Chenal is to dine with us at the episcopal table tonight."

The man's cure was permanent and in a short time was able to resume the labors of the priesthood.

Upon another occasion a paralysed boy, Etienne, was taken to the Bishop's residence by some poor people of Maurienne. Francis was immediately notified of the new arrivals.

"All I can do," he told M. Rolland, "is to pray

to God on the lad's behalf. Bring the people in."

Francis was just about to begin Mass so he suggested that the people place the boy upon the credence table. Having heard his confession, the Bishop proceeded to celebrate Holy Mass. Mass finished, Francis bade the people to bring the lad to church the following morning.

"As for you, my child," he said, turning to the lad, "prepare yourself to receive Holy Communion tomorrow, for I will again say Mass for you and pray to God for your well-being."

On the third day after Mass, Francis went towards the boy, and taking him by the shoulders lifted him up. To the joy and delight of all present it was apparent that God had worked a miracle. The child not only stood, unaided, but walked without any assistance. He left for his home on horseback, in full control of his limbs, completely and forever cured.

The last of May, Francis endured a bitter and unexpected loss. His brother Bernard's regiment had been ordered to Piedmont several weeks earlier. The parting between Bernard and his cherished wife, Marie Aimee, had been most poignant as this was the first time during the eight years of their happy married life that they were to suffer a long separation. Theirs had been a heartbroken farewell!

Indeed, they had wept so bitterly that all present had shared their grief. Three weeks later word reached Francis that his brother had died on the first day of his arrival in Piedmont, of a pestilential fever. "He died in the bosom of the Church, fortified by the sacraments received with great piety, under the direction of good Father Juste," so the notification read.

After assuaging his grief, there remained for Francis the painful task of breaking the news to his sister-in-law, Marie Aimee. On first hearing the dreadful tidings she lost consciousness; upon regaining her senses, however, she managed to exclaim, "O, my God, henceforth I will belong to you alone."

It was difficult for her though to realize that never again would she see him in this mortal life, never again hear his voice, never again console him, nor be comforted by him. Thoughts like these caused her tears to flow copiously. It was only in prayer and in the tender affection of her mother, Jane Frances, and the Bishop of Geneva that she found solace.

In the early hours of September the 7th, in the twentieth year of her life, Marie Aimee, who was staying with her mother at the visitation convent, was seized with the pains of a premature delivery, and both mother and child died within a few hours of one another. Immediately after the funeral of his sister-in-law, Francis ordered that his horses be made ready for a journey. His servants believed that he was preparing to go to Sales' castle where Mother de Chantal was to spend a few days putting things in order.

Francis, however, traveled to Belley, saying to his surprised friends, "You do wrong in thinking Mother de Chantal is in deeper sorrow than I am and that I might console her. I know her strength of soul and my own weakness: how should I give her consolation when I am in much greater need of it than she is? And so, do not blame me if I go to seek it where I believe I shall find it." In John Paul Camus, Francis found sympathy and strength against his double sorrow.

In the midst of his numerous occupations and sorrows, Francis found time to devote to the affairs of the Visitation Order. Too, he received a number of requests for foundations in other French cities and here he acted with great prudence and wisdom.

"Little and well," he remarked smilingly to an importunate visitor who almost demanded that the holy Bishop establish a house in a distant city. "Let us have patience and we will do well enough if the little we do be pleasing to our Master. It is better for our Sisters to increase by the roots of virtues than by the branches of houses. They will not be the more perfect by having a great number of monasteries."

One afternoon, about May 1617, the Bishop was visiting his Visitandine daughters in their convent when Mother de Chantal spoke of two subjects who had presented themselves that morning with the greatest ardor.

"We, however, refused to receive them, your lordship," said Mother de Chantal with a playful glance at the rest of the Sisters.

The Sisters nodded approvingly at their Superior.

Francis, sensing that here was something unusual from most cases, asked, "If they were eager to embrace the religious life, why did you and the Sisters refuse your consent?"

Mother de Chantal again spoke with a tolerant smile, "My lord, you would never believe it possible. They laid down certain conditions for their reception. Imagine! Mademoiselle Harney insisted that she be permitted to keep her ear rings, and Mademoiselle de Myans wished to retain a glass ring which she wore on her finger."

Again the Sisters smiled with their superior and sadly shook their heads. Such folly and wordliness!

Francis de Sales was of another mind. "Tomorrow

morning, Mother, I wish you to send these two young ladies to me. If I find signs of a genuine vocation in them I wish you and your community to receive them on my authority."

Mother de Chantal and her Sisters looked at their visitor in amazement.

"My dear Sisters," continued Francis, seeing their looks of surprise, "where is your charity? We must put up with even the silliness of our neighbors."

In less than a week, on Francis' recommendation, the two girls were received into the Visitation Community and in a very short time, after reflecting upon their foolish vanity, and utterly ashamed before God and the Sisters for their ridiculous requests, they put aside their ornaments.

"The perfume of lilies is sweet, but the perfume of virtues is sweeter still," was Francis' only comment when Mother de Chantal humbly acknowledged that the two postulants showed signs of remarkable virtue.

Chapter XV

ALPINE EDELWEISS

THE good people of Grenoble had been so delighted with Francis' Lenten conferences in 1617 that they begged him to return for the Lent of 1618. Again his sermons were most successful; people arrived in crowds to hear him and eagerly listened to his eloquent discourse. Conversions were many and the lukewarm were drawn to practice a more fervent life. When the Bishop left Grenoble in Easter week he stopped at the Grande Chartreuse, only three leagues distant. Dom Bruno d'Affringues was then Prior, and General of the whole Order of St. Bruno's.

"You are most welcome, my lord," said the learned and holy Superior as he greeted Francis graciously and conducted him to a suitable guest-room.

"I hope you will spend a few days with us in our little monastery, true our beloved St. Bernard called our abode a "locum horroris et solitudinis vastae," but I am sure you will enjoy peace and quiet after your busy days in Grenoble," he continued.

"My dear Father, I have always felt that though you dwell in the midst of a frightful desert, it is a desert filled with the atmosphere of intense sacredness and I have been eager to avail myself of an opportunity of imbibing some of the celestial air," remarked Francis.

"To tell the truth, my Bishop," responded Dom Bruno,"ours is a prison, but a prison so holy and venerable that to serve God here in sanctity and righteousness, as we all strive to do, is a very desirable liberty."

"Very nicely said," replied Francis with an approving nod. He was delighted with the superior who was not only a man of profound learning but a religious of deep humility and simplicity.

"Dear Monsignor, it has just occurred to me that tomorrow will be the feast of St. Justin, the Martyr. Our order has always deeply venerated him as one of the great Apologists of the faith so I shall have to leave you and retire to my cell to prepare for Matins according to our rule. Willingly would I have remained with you until the hour for supper had I not this duty to perform. I am sure, my Bishop, that you will wish me to place obedience before hospitality," the Prior concluded with a child-like glance of inquiry at his guest.

"By all means go, my dear Prior. I thoroughly approve of exact observance," said Francis, marveling at the priest's saintly candour.

Just as the Prior was withdrawing from Francis' cell he met the Procuratrix who asked where he was going and where he had left the Bishop of Geneva.

"I have left him in his room," answered the Superior. "I have just left him so that I might recollect myself in my cell before attending Matins. You know that tomorrow will be the feast of St. Justin."

"Really, reverend Father, I am afraid you are forgetting the courtesies of the world. After all, tomorrow is only a feast of our Order. But, such a guest as the Bishop of Geneva we do not have every day in our desert."

"Truly, I never thought of that," exclaimed the holy Prior in a perplexed tone.

"Surely you must be aware that God is well pleased when we offer Him our duties of hospitality and kindness. You will always have time for singing the praises of God, and there will be many opportunities for chanting Matins, later on."

"Yes, yes, you are right, I am at fault," said the Prior.

"Moreover," expatiated the Procuratrix, who should have been a lawyer, "whose position is it to entertain such a prelate if not yours? Too, who could do it better since you are so well-traveled and richly educated?" he asked.

The Prior was thoroughly disconcerted at his evident lack of hospitality, and was about to retrace his steps towards Francis' room. The officer had not yet finished his argument.

"Reverend Father, it will be a disgrace for our whole Order if you leave the Bishop of Geneva alone," he triumphantly concluded.

"My son," said the Prior humbly, "you are right, I am wrong. I shall return to Monsignor de Geneva at once."

"My lord," he said to his visitor who opened the door when the Prior knocked, "on leaving you a few minutes ago I met one of our officials who told me I was guilty of incivility in leaving you alone. I was reminded that I could easily recover my Matins at another time but that we could not always have among us the Bishop of Geneva."

"Who suggested that?" asked Francis in amazement.

"Our procuratrix. And I believe he is right so

I have come straight back to ask your pardon and beg you to excuse my foolishness."

Francis was more delighted with the saintly priest's humility and charm than he would have been at witnessing a miracle. Immediately his quick mind saw a way out of offending the gentle Prior and yet allowing him the happiness of attending Matins.

"With you and with me, dear Father, it is always God first. Perhaps, you will permit me to attend night Office with you," suggested Francis.

A child-like smile lighted the peaceful features of the Prior. "How lovely! A beautiful solution to the difficulty. You will not be left alone but can join us in audience with our King, and I shall not fail in exact observance nor in the laws of hospitality."

*　*　*

April, May and June passed quickly for Francis as he attended to episcopal affairs in Annecy and Visitandine duties in various cities where he had established his Order.

At this time the question arose about the Sisters of the Visitation using the custom prevalent in so many religious houses of saying 'we' and 'our' in place of 'I' and 'my.' Francis keenly realized that the usage frequently played havoc with the rules of grammar but that the custom was an excellent reminder of the poverty and humility so desirable in religious. After pondering the matter he answered Mother de Chantal in a letter:

"The 'we' and 'our' are not unpleasing to me," he wrote. "Nevertheless, this custom must be so moderated that one must not, by too great habit of speaking thus, make faults, sins and imperfections common property and render confessions unintelligible to confessors unused to the monastery. Consequently, it seems sufficient to me to say 'we' and 'our' of that which is really common to all, such as our room, our rosary, our mother, and so on. In other circumstances use 'I'; for example, 'I was not present at 'our' dinner.' "

July was well-booked for Francis as his schedule was filled to the brim with sermons, conferences and speeches. One day was almost typical of another. He was in constant demand and he would not offend anyone by refusing to preach.

One sultry afternoon in the middle of July Francis had officiated and preached in the church of the Franciscan Recollects of Annecy and, tired by his labors and the excessive heat, had gone to his home for a short rest. Between four and five, two Capuchin fathers called him, and in the midst of their visit complained that he had been so busy with the Franciscan Recollects that he had not honored their church with his presence.

Francis had a great veneration for all branches of the Franciscan Order and exclaimed at once, "How right you are. But there is still ample opportunity to remedy my oversight."

Matching his actions to his words he quickly donned his episcopal robes and said, "Come. Let us go to your church."

Arriving at the Franciscan church Francis not only officiated at the evening Benediction but also preached a most soul-stirring sermon on St. Francis of Assisi. The good fathers were deeply moved by the Bishop's self-sacrifice and thanked him from grateful hearts as he bade them good night.

"We were selfish, dear Bishop, in complaining to you about neglecting us. We should not have bothered you after the fatigues of your busy day," said the Provincial who happened to be visiting the house in Annecy.

"You must know, dear Father Bonaventure, that I belong without distinction to every branch of the Franciscan Order, and I have a double bond therewith: in the first place I was named Francis Bonaventure, in the second place your good father has placed me under the further protection of your holy founder by affiliating me to your Order."

For some time Francis had been busy attending to religious affairs concerned with the Abbey of Sixt and the Prior and his monks were so grateful to the holy Bishop for his suggestions and influence that they frequently asked Francis to visit them. In September Francis found that diocesan affairs were going so nicely that he might make the long-promised visit to the monastery.

Leaving Annecy early one bright September morning he and his companions made such splendid progress that they reached St. Jeoire at noon where they broke their journey and stopped at the inn of Monsieur Louis Danthoz for refreshment. The trip had made the travelers hot and thirsty so they asked Monsieur for some light wine.

"Your excellency, I beg a thousand pardons, but the intense heat of August soured the only wine I have. It is not fit to offer to you. May I suggest that you drink only water and thus avoid an occasion of making yourselves ill?"

"Do not trouble yourself unduly, Monsieur Danthoz," said Francis with a smile. "Bring us the wine."

At Francis' request he brought some of the soured liquor in a glass, making numerous apologies as he offered it to the Bishop.

Francis, after blessing it, tasted it and then

handed the glass to the inn-keeper, remarking, "Monsieur, this is very good wine, indeed. You need not be afraid of giving it to your people."

The host, sampling the contents of the glass, was astonished to find that the drink which he had condemned as vinegar had now become an excellent vintage.

"Excuse me, your lordship, for a few moments," begged the excited inn-keeper as he hastened to the stock from which he had drawn the sample. This was found to be equally as good and the delighted man hurried back to his guests with a broad smile and well-filled glasses. "Mon Dieu, a miracle, your Excellency," he announced as he shrewdly calculated the tiny profit he might make by selling the rest of the wine to his neighbors, after his guests had departed.

Arriving at Sixt the following morning, Francis and his attendants were warmly welcomed. Here the Bishop spent several days going over the community rules in great detail. The word quickly circulated that the Bishop of Geneva was visiting the Abbey at Sixt so a number of people from nearby cities hastened to avail themselves of the opportunity of interviewing him. Sometimes as many as two hundred extra meals had to be provided for the persons of rank and distinction who flocked to see Francis. This matter did not escape the notice of the Bishop who feared that the monks would sustain a great loss in having so many extra mouths to feed.

"Do not worry about all these extra meals," he remarked to the Abbot. "I shall beg God to recompense you for all this hospitality."

Immediately a miraculous multiplication took place. The neighboring river furnished fish in such size and quantity as the monks had never before seen. After the departure of Francis and his companions it was found that the store of bread and wine was in no way depleted.

"Truly, our Lord has blessed us for seeking and following the advice of the Good Bishop of Geneva," remarked the Master of Novices to the Dispenser who had returned to the kitchen wide-eyed after a visit to the wine cellar. There he had found that the tun of wine which they had been using all the time of the Bishop's visit still held a goodly supply.

"Do you not think that his lordship is like his favorite Alpine herb, the edelweiss?" asked Father Dispenser slowly and thoughtfully.

"The edelweiss?" questioned the Master of Novices.

Yes, the edelweiss; as you recall the word means noble and white."

"You are right, so very right," approved the Dispenser. "Francis de Sales is grandly noble and radiantly pure, a joy to men and angels."

CHAPTER XVI

FESTOONS OF AMARANTH
AND GARDENIAS

FOR sometime, Victor Emmanuel, Duke of Savoy, had been entertaining the idea of a marriage between his son, Victor Amandeus, Prince of Piedmont and Princess Christine, the charming sister of Louis XIII who had succeeded Henry IV as King of France upon the latter's assassination some years earlier. After probing the opinion of the French Court, and finding it quite favorable, the Duke sent his son Maurice, the Cardinal, on an embassy to Paris, to make a formal petition for the hand of the French princess on behalf of the Duke's heir. To make success certain, Charles Emmanuel sent with his son a retinue of distinguished men among whom were Francis de Sales and his close friend, Antoine Favre.

The royal party left for France in the middle of October and after a leisurely and thoroughly delightful journey through Grenoble, Lyons, Orleans and Chartres, where they were most flatteringly entertained, they arrived in Paris on November 7th.

From a letter written at the time by Antoine

Favre to the Duke of Savoy the triumphant entry becomes alive:

"I cannot hide from Your Highness all the pleasure which I experienced yesterday, when our Cardinal, your son, in the midst of much splendor and pageantry, made his solemn entry into Paris. Placed in the same carriage as the Bishop of Geneva, I compared my position to that of the younger Pliny, when seated by the side of the great Tacitus at the public games. Among the vast throng of spectators who crowded around us there was not one acquainted with theology and law who did not hasten to point us out and exclaim, 'There is the Bishop of Geneva, the greatest theologian of the day; and here is President Favre who has published so many books and is like a brother to Francis de Sales in the deep love and unique friendship which unites them to each other.'

Last evening, after we were most comfortably established in the former home of Marshal d'Ancre in the rue de Tournon, a mansion now used exclusively for ambassadorial purposes, Cardinal Maurice was received in private audience by Louis. Francis de Sales and I, housed with your son, did not accompany him last evening, but tonight accompanied by his entire suite, Maurice was granted an official reception by Louis XIII and his wife,

Anne. I already feel sure, my lord, that your son will manage everything most satisfactorily."

When Francis was not engaged in attending official functions he was in great demand as a preacher, invitation succeeded invitation; he refused none. On December 2nd he opened the Advent season in the church of St. Andrew where the crowd of people who had assembled to hear him was so great that even cardinals, bishops and princes found it difficult to obtain places among the congregation. Francis took the idea for this initial sermon from the eleventh book of "The Love of God" and his listeners were so captivated by his earnestness and knowledge of the vital truths of charity that they realized they were listening to no mere orator but to a saint.

"Pliny assures us," said the Bishop, "that he saw at Tivoli a tree engrafted in every kind of way and bearing several sorts of fruits; one branch was laden with cherries, another with nuts, some produced grapes and figs, others pomegranates, apples and several other fruits. This was an astonishing and beautiful example of the variety of nature; but still more admirable is that which faith gives us, when it represents in man the divine virtue of charity, on which all others are engrafted. As the tree of which Pliny speaks produced many kinds of fruit at the same time, so charity may be said to be at once gentle, powerful, patient, and just; or rather, meekness, sanctity and fortitude itself.

"Now there is still a great difference between this virtue and the tree," explained Francis as he warmed to his holy subject, "because, as Pliny assures us, the bloom of the latter was transient, the great variety of its productions exhausted its radical moisture, so that it soon withered and died. It is not so with charity; on the contrary, the variety and abundance of its fruits serve to strengthen it; the more it is exercised in all virtues, the more it multiplies their acts, and the more its vigor increases."

When Francis had concluded his sermon and given Benediction he noticed the enthusiasm of his audience and marveled that the people of the great French capital should be so spell-bound by the utterances of a 'provincial bishop,' as he styled himself.

"Are you not amazed," he asked Pere Binet who accompanied him to rue de Tournon, "to see all these good Parisians coming to hear me—me, whose tongue is so awkward, whose words are so common and ordinary, whose ideas are so matter-of-fact and whose sermons are really quite dull?"

"Do you think," asked Pere Binet with a smile

at the holy Bishop, "that it is fine words they come to hear from you? My esteemed friend, it is enough for them to see you in the pulpit; your heart, aflame with divine love, speaks to them from both your eyes and your mouth. Your simple language, burning with the fire of charity, goes straight to their hearts and moves them. You possess something that none of our illustrious court preachers have, let us call it the rhetoric of Paradise," Pere Binet stated gracefully.

During the busy month of December the marriage negotiations were moving to a successful issue but not without a certain amount of friction in regard to details. In these negotiations Francis played an important part and on one occasion, when the whole idea was almost called off by Louis, Francis with his persuasion and patience, adroitly saved the situation.

Francis conceived a great esteem and admiration for Princess Christine who though only thirteen was accomplished, dignified and gracious. Tall for her age, brown-eyed, slim, and graceful in every movement she was as renowned for her modesty and devotion in religious matters as for her beauty and kindness of character. The Bishop of Geneva was very happy when on the 18th of the month he was able to write to the Duke that the desired marriage was almost a certainty and there remained only one or two details to be settled.

In the midst of his preaching and official duties Francis found time to arrange for the foundation of a Visitation Convent in Paris. Earlier in the year, Pope Paul V had sent the founder a Bull, authorizing him to form into a religious order the Visitation Institute so Francis was able to give his new daughters their rules and constitutions at once, without being obliged to make them wait for several years as the earlier subjects had been forced to do.

On Christmas Eve, Francis celebrated Mass and gave Holy Communion to the French Queen, Anne of Austria, and preached before her and her whole court. To show Mother de Chantal how adverse he was to receiving favors from royalty he later made a pithy remark, "Do not imagine, dear Mother, that any favor of the court can hold me. How much more desirable it is to be poor in the house of God than to dwell in the great palaces of kings. I am undergoing my novitiate of court life, but, with the help of God, I shall never make my profession therein."

During the Christmastide final details of the marriage settlement were satisfactorily arranged and late in January the Prince of Piedmont, happy and eager to be in Paris left Chambery in company with his younger brother, Thomas. Finding the boat trip down the Loire from Lyons to Roanne too slow they disembarked at Bony and made the remainder of the trip by carriage, arriving in a very gay Paris on the evening of February 7th. Victor Amadeus immediately thanked his brother, the Cardinal, and Francis de Sales profusely for their part in concluding the negotiations so happily and spent the next two days in preparing for the big event.

February the 10th marked the celebration of the royal marriage in the chapel of the Louvre before Cardinal de la Rochefoucauld, Grand Almoner of France, who was assisted by the Bishop of Geneva. The young bride had chosen amaranth as her color and with that enviable French touch the lovely little chapel was so richly adorned that it glowed like an exquisite royal jewel in its rich purple setting. Festoons of amaranth and gardenias hung from the high walls and formed a fragrant aisle for the bridal party. The ten days following the nuptials were devoted to all kinds of court festivities, each succeeding entertainment rivaling the former in lavish display. Immense sums of money were spent while hosts and guests ate, drank and made merry.

Francis, however, very seldom took part in any of the celebrations as he was busily winning converts and making new friends. It was with the Calvinists in Paris that Francis had experiences similar to those he encountered in the Chablais. At least a half dozen of the more illustrious Huguenots who called on the holy Bishop to trip him in his arguments were so won by his logical mind and kind attitude towards their errors that he completely won them back to the true fold. Sometimes the callers' arguments were ridiculous; oftentimes pathetic, but Francis always exhibited tireless patience and tact, and had the glorious satisfaction of setting their minds at ease, and of enjoying the stimulating tonic of triumphing over wrong.

One evening as the late February sun "stooped to gather up his spent shafts and place them back in his golden quiver" a little, wizened apple of an Huguenot called at rue de Tournon and asked to see the Bishop of Geneva.

"Are you the man they call the Bishop of Geneva?" he brusquely demanded as a servant admitted him to Francis' apartment.

Francis noticing the rudeness of the stranger and scenting trouble answered mildly, "I am so called, Monsieur, although I am allowed little access to that city."

To the amazement of the Bishop, the Calvinist stated, "Sir, I should like to know from you directly, doubtless you are aware of the fact that most people describe you as an apostolic man, as to whether or not the apostles went about in carriages?"

Quickly recovering from his surprise Francis answered, "Yes, at times when it was necessary the Apostles made use of carriages."

The caller looking at Francis steadily asked, "Can you prove that to me from Scripture?"

"In the Acts of the Apostles the account is given of the deacon Philip entering the chariot of the Queen's eunuch, when the latter invited him to do so," answerd Francis without hesitation.

"The carriage did not belong to St. Philip but to the eunuch who invited him to ride with him," objected the Huguenot.

"I did not state that the carriage belonged to him, merely that when the occasion arose, the Apostles made use of these vehicles," responded Francis calmly.

"But what you do not find in the Scriptures," said the visitor shaking his head sadly, "is that they rode in carriages decorated with gold, and so luxurious that the Kings had no better. This is what scandalizes me; you play the saint yet use a conveyance driven by a coachman in the finest liveries and drawn by the most splendid horses. A fine saint indeed! One who is driven to heaven most comfortably!"

"Monsieur, I have never had a carriage of my own, nor even the means to keep one," said Francis.

"Am I to understand that the gorgeous carriage in which I see you going each day through town, does not belong to you?" questioned the astonished caller.

"Indeed, no. It belongs to Louis XIII. It is one of several which the king so thoughtfully ordered for those who, like myself, are attached to the suite of Victor Amadeus. You surely should have known that by the royal livery worn by the driver."

"I am pleased to hear you say this," admitted the Huguenot. "Then you are really poor?"

"I make no complaint of my poverty," replied Francis. "I have enough to live decently, without any superfluity."

"I shall always hold you in the greatest esteem, Sir. I am delighted that I have made your acquaintance," stated the Protestant as he left Francis more courteously than he met him.

Another evening some ladies of distinction called on Francis just after he had returned from preaching in the Church of St. Andrew. Every one had a different question to ask him, or wished the solution of a difficulty, and all at once.

Francis was at a loss as how to reply to them all, when an ingenious solution to the dilemma presented itself.

With a smile at each importunate visitor he amiably asked, "I will answer all your questions, provided you will reply to one of mine."

"Yes, indeed, yes," they murmured in unison.

"In a company where all speak, and none listens, pray can you tell me what is said?" he asked.

Non-plussed, the Parisians glanced at one another in embarrassment. Francis, seeing that they grasped the point at once, suggested that each take a turn asking about her particular difficulty. Needless to say, the interview passed most satisfactorily for all concerned.

Among the many notable men of the day who became friends with Francis at this time was Vincent de Paul who contracted the closest ties of affection with the visiting prelate. An irresistible force seemed to draw the two holy souls together. Vincent so highly admired the beautiful character of the holy Bishop that upon more than one occasion he was heard to exclaim, "What must Thou be, O my God, if the Bishop of Geneva, who is but a man, is so good?"

In turn, Francis esteemed Vincent's piety and rare wisdom so sincerely that he made him Spiritual Director of the Visitation Convent in Paris, an office he discharged for about forty years with a wisdom which so approved itself to the Holy Founder, that he was used to say that he knew no worthier priest than Vincent.

During the warm August days the French Court and the Court of Charles Emmanuel retired to Fontainebleau. The change was most fortunate for Francis as the extreme July heat had been too intense for him and he was severely ill for some days. His health, however, soon improved when he was away from the busy, dusty city in the open country where the air was fresher and cooler, and he was not in constant demand for conferences and ceremonial functions. At Fontainebleau he was able to enjoy the great open spaces, trees, birds, and above all, the flowers.

It was at this royal residence that Cardinal de Retz sought Francis one delightfully lazy afternoon when most of the inhabitants of the palace seemed to be enjoying a long, leisurely siesta. After looking in vain for him in the royal chapel the Cardinal found Francis in his second favorite spot—the royal gardens, resting on one of the lovely, rustic benches. A shimmer of soft golden sunshine rested on the bishop's episcopal cross, lighting his smiling countenance as he keenly enjoyed the luxuriant beauty surrounding him. The Cardinal paused for a moment before he broke the solemn stillness. In the near distance sunlight and shadow played on the ivy-mantled towers of the castle while the spicy scent of carnations and the heady perfume of roses drifted on the cooling breezes.

"Am I intruding, my lord? questioned the Archbishop of Paris as he quietly approached the enchanted Bishop of Geneva.

Francis slightly raised his head to welcome his guest and exclaimed, "How happy I am to have someone enjoy the wonderous beauty with me, and I am most happy that it is your excellency who is to share it."

"How can anyone see nature at its best and fail to see the Almighty Hand that designs and guides it?" asked the Cardinal.

"I have been thinking that it takes forty thousand of these glorious full-blown roses to make one ounce of Attar of Roses. Try to imagine what an immense amount of concentrated fragrance an ounce of this exotic perfume contains! Do you know, the thought just occurred to me that creating a fine personality is similar to making Attar of Roses; the former calls for concentrating in our lives the essence of the best and finest life has to offer. Forty thousand acts of love, forty thousand acts of kindness, forty thousand smiles, forty thousand aspirations, really the thought is appalling! Such fine personalities perfume the sphere of their influence with a fragrance that is uncalculated," said Francis as his eyes sparkled with the thought.

"And how gloriously happy those people with fine personalities are. Did you by chance read the statement one of those English writers made? 'Happiness is a perfume which you cannot pour on others without spilling a few drops on yourself?' " quoted the Archbishop.

"How very true and truly beautiful," exclaimed Francis approvingly.

"My dear Bishop, I need your assistance. That is why I am disturbing you this afternoon in your quiet retreat. No, not this minute," he added, as Francis started to rise from his bench. "I am overburdened with my numerous duties, first as Minister of State and secondly as head of the King's Council. Will you, my very dear friend, accept the charge of Coadjutor with the right of succeeding me?" he pleaded.

"Your excellency, have you forgotten that I have a diocese of my own?" playfully countered Francis.

"I will arrange that the bishopric of Geneva shall be given to your brother," responded the prelate immediately. "Moreover, I shall undertake to obtain the consent of the King of France and the Duke of Savoy for these plans to be executed at once. Too, I shall supply all the expenses necessary for legal papers and apostolic letters from Rome."

Cardinal de Retz," said Francis, "I —"

"Wait," interrupted the Archbishop, "You cannot fail to have noticed how much you are beloved by the people of Paris. Consequently, you cannot doubt but that you will be able to effect the same useful work here in the future that you have already accomplished here in the past months."

"I thank you with all my heart for the honor you are showing me, my lord, for the kindness of your invitation," replied Francis, after he was certain that the Cardinal had finished his plea. "I, however, must refuse the offered dignity, as I feel that it is the will of God for me to remain in Annecy."

"I do not," challenged the Archbishop. "This office I beg you to accept will be for the greater glory of God. In addition, I protest, my dear Bishop, that you would place me under infinite obligations if you will only deign to accept it."

"If I should ever resign my bishopric, Cardinal de Retz," said Francis touched by the sincerity of the Cardinal's request, "I shall lay aside the burdens of the episcopacy forever. The state of my health and the advance of old age make the office you so graciously tender altogether impossible for me to accept as the work in Paris would be much heavier than in the Duchy of Savoy. Again, I thank you for your generous offer. Now, my lord, shall we repair to the chapel together? I promised to give the Queen and her ladies Benediction at five."

The time for the departure of the Prince of Piedmont and his royal suite was drawing near and many Parisians who had benefited by the guidance and friendship of the Bishop of Geneva were grieved at the thought of losing him. He tried to console them in some measure by writing them exquisite letters of farewell, raising their hearts to God and telling each that one who belongs wholly to God is never saddened. He closed most of his notes writing, "With all my heart I bid you adieu; I commend you to God."

To the Countess of Ville-Savin he wrote the most beautiful words of all, "Do not imagine that wide distances can separate souls whom God has united in the ties of charity. We shall see each other very often before the holy crucifix and there indeed it is that meetings are solely and completely for our good. Often, when I was in Padua I thought of my dear father, mother, brothers and sister. Do you know what eased my longing for them? The thought that the same stars that were shining in God's clear Italian sky were gleaming over Savoy and that we both gazed at the selfsame stars with loving, though lonely, eyes."

The countess' reply to Francis was remarkable,

"Each night whatever stars may shine
In French or Savoyard 'rue'
Remember I am watching them
And you may watch them too;
The same white stars that shine on me,
Those same shall shine on you,
And I shall place on every star
A nightly prayer for you."

September the 13th was the day set for the departure of the Prince and his Princess with their retinue. Though all were eager to journey directly to Geneva it was necessary to go to Tours, where the King and his Queen mother had retired, in order to bid them a final farewell. Here three days were passed in ceremonial receptions and festivities. The King and Catherine de Medici showed marked kindness again to Francis and Cardinal de Retz repeated his invitation that Francis remain in France. On the 17th the group were able to leave Tours, and by slow stages passed through Amboise, Bourges, Moulin, Lyons and Grenoble eventually reaching Annecy on the 31st of October.

On the feast of All Saints, the well-traveled bishop again resumed his episcopal duties as though there had been no long interruption. His correspondence of November and December of this year shows the extraordinary multiplicity of his varied interests.

Chapter XVII

BLAZING POPPIES

HAPPINESS and blessedness were part and parcel of Francis' life; his happiness was increased by removing the wretchedness from others' lives, and the blessing of God fell daily like dew on his tonsured head enabling him, though far from well, to continue during the winter and spring of 1621 his many ecclesiastical duties.

Monsieur Martin, whom Francis had met at La Roche in 1605 and taken to Annecy with him, had so thoroughly profited by the good Bishop's care and instructions during the sixteen years that he was part of the episcopal household that he had not only acquired a knowledge of the mysteries of the Catholic religion but he could show by signs the difference between mortal and venial sin, the evil effects of the seven capital sins and could make an excellent confession to his spiritual father. When the poor deaf mute heard daily Mass his reverence was profound and when he received Holy Communion his devotion was a source of edification to all observers. During the course of the years his affection for Francis had waxed so strong that when the Bishop returned to Annecy after his long sojourn in the French capital the poor man ran like a child to welcome his beloved protector and by a thousand signs manifested his sincere joy in having him home once again.

Francis showed the poor soul every delicate attention possible, and frequently invited him to the Bishop-Prince Apartments when distinguished visitors called. On one of the evenings in early March a number of distant prelates had been guests at the evening meal, which was a simple collation since it was Lent. It was the first time the priests had seen their bishop since his return to Annecy and diocesan matters took a good part of the time. Later in the night, however, after official business was completed, Francis summoned Monsieur Martin to the room and suggested that he preach to the company. Immediately the deaf man sat down in his comfortable arm chair and admonished his audience with a sermon of inarticulate sounds. The subject was on the gravity of vice. To show the seriousness of evil he would turn towards the fire and make gestures to show that sinners would be plunged into hell's fires, to illustrate the rewards of virtue he would eloquently raise his eyes and hands towards heaven to demonstrate the crown awaiting the just.

One of the guests admiring this marvelous display said, "My lord, why, since your prayers and kindliness have done so much for this poor man, do you not restore speech and hearing to him?"

"I must say," answered Francis, "that I have never had any inclination to ask God for this miracle. Too, it is useful for me to have someone towards whom I can practice a little charity each day."

Towards the end of June, Francis though not at all well, received a visit from his very dear friend John Paul Camus and his health improved sufficiently for a little excursion on the Lake of Annecy. The hot days of August, however, were hard on the Bishop of Geneva and he wrote to Mother de Chantal that for eight or nine days he had been experiencing those little indispositions which the summer usually brought him

The fruitful month of September brought vim and vigor to Francis who decided that since he was feeling so very much better he would return the Bishop of Belley's call.

Early one evening when the 'fairy clock had struck its inaudible hour and each punctual flower in field and garden had hastened to obey its summons and had gone to sleep,' the Bishop of Geneva announced to M. Rolland, "Tomorrow, my dear friend, you and I shall go to Belley to see John Paul whom I find ever more and more charming."

The visit was, as usual, most delightful, and after two blessed days which not all Apollo's Pythian treasures could prolong, the Bishop of Geneva bade farewell to his intimate friend and left for Annecy, stopping at several cities where parochial matters needed his attention. As Francis and his companion skirted one tiny village to shorten ther journey, they passed a field blazing with bell-like scarlet poppies. It was a breath-taking sight for the holy Bishop who reveled in the beauties of nature.

Reining in his horse he spoke to M. Rolland, "How lovely those bright poppies are! They bravely raise their brilliant heads in any soil; one finds them in the cultivated gardens of the wealthy, in the tiny, poorly-kept plots of the poor, and growing luxuriantly and riotously in the great, open fields. Truly, dear friend, a lesson for us in adaptation."

"Yes, my lord, but how quickly they wither and die, once they are plucked."

"Another lesson for us, Monsieur," said Francis as he voiced the thought later immortalized by the poet Burns, pleasures are like poppies, exquisite to gaze upon, but once possessed the bloom, or glamour, is shed.

With a tiny sigh and final glance at the glorious field, the riders urged their horses on, and after a few miles of pleasant countryside they reached Evian.

Francis had heard a number of complaints about the scandalous life of one of the ecclesiastics of this city. The whole affair was most unfortunate as the priest was a man of unusual talents and great learning, He had, however, become so defiant, that he not only protested his innocence before Francis, when summoned to an interview with his Bishop, but he even condemned his accusers. Francis, with his usual kindness and calmness listened to the poor wretch's effrontery, but he could not conceal the pain in his heart and blushed with shame and sorrow at the man's hardened conscience.

The sight of the Bishop's sorrow touched the heart of the sinner and he fell on his knees and begged, "My lord, grace has touched my heart. You have uttered no word of reproach to me. I am sincerely ashamed of myself. Please permit me to make my confession to you, now."

Francis, overjoyed, complied with the priest's request.

Confession over, the penitent turned to Francis

and asked, "Ah, Bishop, what do you think of me, the greatest sinner upon earth?"

"I think that God has overshadowed you with his greatest favors," replied Francis. "To me, you appear all refulgent with grace."

"But you know what I am," humbly pleaded the priest.

"You are just what I say," answered Francis.

"But, my lord, I allude to the past."

"That, my dear father, is just what I have no recollection of. Why should I remember what God has forgotten? Do you take me for the Pharisee who looked upon Magdalen as she had been, not as she was when she bathed our Lord's feet in her tears?"

The mortified and repentent man sobbed softly.

"Moreover," continued Francis, "to convince you that I look upon you as replenished with celestial graces, whereof you have received a measure full and overflowing, I beg of you to share them with me by giving me your blessing."

Francis at once threw himself on his knees before the priest who hurriedly begged his Bishop to arise.

"No, no, I am in earnest," said Francis. "I expect you to return to me the same good office I have rendered to you."

In vain did the embarrassed priest protest. He

had to obey his superior who made his confession to him. Thereafter the priest led a holy, religious life.

Towards the end of November Francis was summoned to Sixt where the Abbot lay dying. Despite the severe winter which had already set in, and the hardships of mountain travel, the Bishop left Annecy at once and arrived at the monastery in time to fortify the dying monk by the last sacraments and to assist him in his final moments.

Although Francis stated to his friends in mid-December that his health was greatly improved, at the beginning of the New Year he was again far from well. His legs were once more swollen and covered with sores so that at times he could scarcely walk. Too, he was afflicted with violent pains in his head and back, but in the midst of all his sufferings he preserved his remarkable cheerfulness and patience.

The spring of 1622 brought Francis a sweet consolation in the form of Charles Augustus de Sales, the son of his beloved brother Louis. It had been decided that the lad, condemned to perpetual lameness because of the carelessness of an early nurse, should become a member of the Bishop's household and study under his direction. Charles Augustus gave early evidence of a brilliant mind and before he was eight had read "The Introduction to a Devout Life" so thoroughly and frequently, that he knew it practically by heart.

One morning he approached his estimable uncle in great distress and said sorrowfully, "Uncle, I am ashamed of being so little worthy of being your nephew."

"My, my," exclaimed Francis indulgently, "what is troubling my little lad?"

"I know so little, and unless you help me a great deal, I am likely to remain utterly ignorant all my life."

Francis, delighted with the child's thirst for education, secured for him the best tutors and undertook, himself, the spiritual education of the boy. "The youth is born for great things," he remarked to his brother Louis, "and it is God's wish that his mind should be carefully cultivated."

Another day, during instruction, he said to his nephew, "Remember, my dear child, that God has chosen you to be a vessel of grace and that, if you are faithful to follow his inspirations, he will make great use of you for His service."

About this time Francis, concluding that the lad was destined for the priesthood, said to Louis, "If God wills that this lad, who is yours by nature and mine by love, should live a long time, I should like to instil into his mind everything that God's grace has put into mine."

With his brother's consent, the lad received the tonsure. Many years later, as a priest he wrote the finest biography of Francis that was ever written.

During these busy times the Visitation Order was progressing wonderfully well. In February, Mother de Chantal left the Parisian house in the hands of capable Sisters and made a brief visit at Orleans, Bourges, Nevers and Allonne, while she was awaiting the Sisters Francis was to send to her for the foundation of a monastery at Dijon. Later, at the repeated request of John Paul Camus, a Visitation house was opened at Belley.

In May, Francis was summoned to preside over the election of a Superior for the Order of the Feuillants, an offshot of the Cistercians, at Pignerol. His friends, realizing that the busy man was far from well tried to persuade him to refuse to attend the Chapter.

"I must obey," he repeatedly said. "I have only a short time to live now and I must hasten to do all the good I can."

The Chapter opened on May 30th and continued with its deliberations until the 19th of June. During these overly-busy weeks Francis' strength was taxed to the utmost with the inevitable result that one evening, overcome by heat, weariness and exhaustion, he fainted. Great was the consternation of the priests who feared that the life of the holy Bishop was in eminent danger.

Great was their joy, when after a few moments, Francis recovered consciousness and whispered quietly, "What a poor servant I am of He who was crowned with thorns."

His work at Pignerol completed, Francis went on to Turin at the express command of Princess Christine who, wishing to show every mark of esteem and honor to her saintly chaplain, had ordered magnificent apartments prepared for him. At once, Francis begged that he might be permitted to stay with the Feuillants during his sojourn in the city as he abhorred ostentation and display as much as he approved simplicity and holy poverty. His visit at the house of the Feuillants was much longer than he had anticipated when he took up his residence in the tiny cell the good fathers so apologetically offered to him.

"Permit me to have the consolation of living a few days with you as your brother," he had asked when the superior had stated that the only room available at the time was a tiny one exposed to the full heat of the glaring summer sun during most of the day.

So highly did the good fathers revere their saintly guest that on the 24th of June they conferred on him an extraordinary privilege, the grant of letters which testified Francis affiliation with the Order of Feuillants. It was not until the 17th of August that Francis was able to take formal leave of the Princess Christine who presented her chaplain with a very magnificent ring. It was one of the few times Francis accepted a valuable gift, and he did so only because he knew that his people in Annecy were enduring the sufferings of famine and the ring might be sold to buy nourishment for his flock.

Just as Francis and his companion were leaving Turin they met Monsieur Jean de Corsier who wished them God-speed.

"I am leaving Turin with great happiness and I am resolved, on reaching Annecy, to sell all that I have, mitre, crozier, clothes and plate in order to alleviate the sufferings of my dear people," said Francis as he bade farewell to his newly-made friend.

After they had journeyed a short distance the startling discovery was made by M. Rolland that the Princess' ring could not be found. Francis accepted the news with his usual calmness but his companion searched high and low for the brilliant jewel.

"Do not distress yourself, M. Rolland," remarked Francis. "That ring was far too valuable for my use. If we do not find it, it only means that God wishes to spare us the trouble of using in almsgiving the money we should have obtained for it. Moreover, Providence might intend to make the fortune of some indigent person."

Strange to say, the ring was not lost, but later that evening M. Rolland found it in the fold of the Bishop's cloak. Immediately upon reaching Annecy, Francis sent the ring to the jeweler's to be sold in order to obtain funds for his needy. Monsieur Giselle, hearing of the sale at once redeemed the valuable bauble and returned it to Francis. Again Francis sold the Princess' gift, and again another friend bought it and returned it to the Bishop. Thus the little sales went on ad infinitum, until eventually the populace of Annecy bestowed upon the magnificent jewel the humble appellation—'the beggar's ring.'

October with its sunset skies and painted leaves found Francis' health in a precarious condition, though he continued to perform his priestly duties and visit the many, many sick. On one of his pastoral calls, at the home of the lawyer, Monsieur P. Gard, he met the advocate's wife who was holding her sick child in her arms.

"What is wrong with your little daughter?" kindly questioned Francis as he noted the look of anguish in the good mother's eyes.

"Alas, your lordship, for three months now, my little girl has been suffering from a slow fever. My husband and I pray daily that she be restored to health. Surely, our poor prayers are not said in vain!"

Francis reached down and lightly touching the sick child's cheek blessed her and said, "May God Almighty cure you, my dear child."

Scarcely had the saintly visitor left the lawyer's home when little Josephine Gard explained in a voice filled with animation, "Mother, I am cured. The moment the Bishop touched me I felt all well."

Mrs. Gard glanced hastily at her daughter and found that she was indeed well. In fact, she was never again sick.

CHAPTER XVIII

THE PALM, PRINCE OF TREES

On a particularly melancholy November day, when the meadows lay brown and sere after yielding their rich autumnal harvest, Francis received a royal summons at his episcopal residence to accompany Charles Emmanuel to Avignon where the Duke of Savoy and the French King, Louis XIII were to meet to discuss certain matters of mutual interest.

When Francis' numerous friends learned of the proposed journey they were decidedly worried and were not slow in voicing their protests. Alone and in groups they pleaded with their Bishop to send his excuses to the Duke.

"If you yourself will not write to his Excellency, permit me to send a messenger, telling him of the state of your health," begged Monsieur de Crillon.

"The inconveniences and privations of traveling will undermine the little health you now have," argued Francis' brother, Louis.

"I shall have no one to instruct me in moral theology!" coaxed Charles Augustus who had been coached by his father to ask Francis to remain in Annecy.

"The inclemency of the winter season at Avignon will be too severe for your strength," reminded Monsieur Oiseau.

To each and all of his solicitous friends and relatives Francis made only one answer, "We must go where God calls us, that is the voice of obedience. We must keep on as long as we can."

Francis had a premonition that he would never again see his beloved Annecy so before he left he placed all his affairs in order, made his will, and handed over to his coadjutor all documents and reports of importance. He then devoted a morning to the care of his soul.

On the eighth of November beneath a veil of fine rain Francis called at the Visitation Convent for a farewell visit. Having celebrated Mass for the Sisters' intentions, Francis presented them with a rich chausable, which had been given to him by the Princess of Savoy.

"When friends part, they usually exchange gifts, you recall," he reminded them with one of his charming smiles.

For a few moments he spoke to them in tenderly appealing words of the love of God and zeal for souls. He concluded his little exhortation by saying, "Let your one and only desire, my dear daughters, be to love God; your only ambition be to possess Him. Farewell until eternity, my very dear daughters."

"Dear Father, we shall pray God to bring you back to us," the Sisters cried with tear-dimmed eyes.

"And if God does not wish to bring me back, are we to bless Him any the less?" he asked as they knelt for his blessing.

That same day as the late afternoon shadows were falling over the city Francis set out for Lyons, one of the first stops on the journey to Avignon. As the little group were leaving the city gates near the blue-green waters of Lake Annecy, Francis begged his friends who were accompanying him as far as Seyssel to rein in their horses so that he might bid a final farewell to the cherished scene of his episcopal labors for twenty prolific years. In the far distance stood the Visitation convent, its mellow, red brick walls warm under a late fall mantle of bright morning glories. Scattered far and wide throughout the city were palatial homes, smaller dwellings of stone, and cottages of mud with thatched roofs. On the west were the old prison, Palais de L'ile, the little stucco Gallery House, scarcely discernable down Rue de la Providence, and numerous parish churches, all places poignantly dear and familiar to the departing Bishop of Geneva.

As the riders turned due west the lines of a little poem, written by one of his Visitandine daughters and presented to him on the eve of his departure, repeated themselves in Francis' mind:

> A vine with blooms of azure hue,
> Twines on our convent's wall;
> Other flowers are growing near,
> But this vine's surpasses all.
>
> For the morning glory in mantle blue
> Thrives best in broad day-light;
> Other blossoms stay awake
> Throughout the long, dark night.
>
> But when the twilight hovers near,
> And comes in sandals gray,
> Blue petals curl on yellow heart,
> And feign would sleep away,
>
> Until the brilliant morning sun
> With warm and golden ray,
> Kissing tightly-folded flowers,
> Proclaims a new-born day.

On leaving Seyssel, after his friends had bidden him an adieu mingled with love and sorrow, Francis continued with only Canon Rolland, the Canon of la Roche and two servants. Guided by the love of God, and guarded by the virtue of holy poverty "they traveled safely and not unpleasantly." Frequently, the glowing landscape atoned for an indifferent meal, and the charming courtesies obliterated the remembrances of uncomfortable beds.

Arriving at Lyons, the bishop found Mother de Chantal awaiting him. The two friends had not met for four years and there was much to be discussed. As time was very pressing, however, Francis did not remain at the convent more than a few hours, but promised on his return trip to stay over in Lyons for some days.

At Bourg-Saint-Andeol, Francis was ceremoniously greeted by the town's officials and by a great concourse of people who met him at the boat landing, and in a ripple of red, blue, green and brown, proceeded to escort him to the parish church where a Te Deum was chanted because the great bishop had honored the city as a guest. The next morning Francis was conducted by the same colorful cortege to his boat where the citizens overwhelmed him with praise and presents.

"How the rain was pouring in a never-ending
    sheet,
  How it drove beneath the doors!

How it soaked the passers' feet!"

In this torrent Francis and his companions arrived, tired and half frozen, in the crowded city of Avignon. Once again history repeated itself for Francis. He and his friends spent hours before they could find any lodgings in this "city of popes." The French Court and the Court of Savoy were established there for the time, so all the hotels and inns were over-crowded. The waters roared like a turbulent river down the cobble-stone streets to the gutters as the weary bishop and his depressed escorts waded from place to place seeking shelter, only to find everything occupied by lords and ladies who had flocked to Avignon to bask in the royal favor of Anne of Austria, Marie de Medici and Louis XIII. In the late evening, tiny quarters were secured through the tireless efforts of a compatriot.

During the days that followed, Francis attended the public festivities as seldom as courtesy permitted. While the rest of the people were following in the royal footsteps he remained in his rooms, accessible to all. Nearly every day he said Mass in one of the churches or convents in the city.

During the last week of November, Louis, greatly pleased with the events, planned with the assistance of his favorite De Luy, a hunt for the two courts.

Early on the clear morning of November the 22nd, the train of hunters (murmuring a swift prayer to St. Eustace, patron of the chase,) rode from the royal gates. A pack of hounds, eager for the chase, were followed by the mounted sportsmen, each with his trained panther sitting behind him, on the saddle. Hosts of pages, in colorful apparel, with ribbons fluttering in the cool breeze, trotted next. When the royal parties had reached the scene of the hunt, the dogs took up the chase and then the panthers jumped from the saddles to spring after the prey.

Charles Emmanuel tossed a piece of raw flesh to his panther who seemed to be the swiftest in the chase. The panther caught the meat, dragged the captured animal to his master and remounted alert for more booty.

"Well done, my lord," shouted Louis as he galloped by.

"May it be your turn next, your Highness," answered the Duke.

After a glorious morning spent in the great out-of-doors, the two parties cantered back to Avignon where Marie de Medici, Anne of Austria, and her sister-in-law, Elizabeth, welcomed them to a royal breakfast.

"That table-cloth you are using," Marie de Medici

whispered to her daughter-in-law, "was given to me at the time of my marriage. My mother bought it in 1572 when Count Ferrara's goods were sold, after his sudden death. She thought it so exquisite that she didn't mind buying it second-hand. It's the first time I have seen you use it, my dear."

"I have heard how Catherine outbid all rivals for the linen. Yes, I use it on only very important occasions. Today is one, you know. Louis is well-pleased with his parley with the Duke of Savoy."

Paint, patches and perfumes, all introduced by the de Medici family, were then the height of fashion as was evidenced by the ladies paying adulation to the three queens. What a gay, glittering, magnificent party it was. Pomp and splendor were every where in evidence, but—Francis de Sales was not!

The Bishop of Geneva had declined the invitation as he had wished to say Mass at the chapel of St. Praxedes on that morning and later attend the Office of St. Cecelia, sung by the nuns. St. Cecelia, patroness of church music, was one of his favorite Martryrs, and he always attended in his own cathedral, when opportunity permitted, all the offices of her feast day.

On the 25th of the month the royal negotiations and festivities ended. The Duke, too, was delighted with the favorable results and presented Louis with three magnificent horses, a sword of famed Damascan make and a shield gleaming with diamonds and emeralds.

When the two courts left Avignon they rode on to Lyons where they arrived four days later. Distinguished people disputed with one another as to who would have the honor of housing the Bishop of Geneva. Monsieur Jacques Olier, Intendant of the Province, offered the half of his house if only he might have the privilege of entertaining Francis. To his numerous invitations Francis made a firm but courteous refusal. He knew where he wished to stay.

When he reached the Visitation Convent he asked his spiritual daughters to occupy a little room in the gardener's cottage, located on the grounds near the gate. This room, usually reserved for the Sisters' confessor, was small, cold and had a very smoky chimney, frequently bearded with cob-webs, as it was abode of a colony of spiders that could not be permanently dislodged. The Sisters protested in vain! Such a dwelling was not fit for the Bishop! Francis argued that living close to the convent his time would be at the Sisters' disposal (a real incentive for them to yield to his request), that being separated from the distractions of the Court he could lead a more recollected life, and that residing in the cottage he would inconvenience no one. His arguments won the day!

When Francis' friends learned where he was staying they again pleaded with him to think of his health and to accept their hospitality. When he remained adamantine, one of his well-wishers sent him a carriage for his use during his stay at Lyons. This attention Francis gracefuly refused, having in mind the attack the Huguenot made on his using the royal carriage some years earlier.

When his friend chided Francis for refusing the use of the vehicle the Bishop thoughtfully replied, "I should look well, Monsieur, going off in a carriage to announce the penitential preaching of St. John and the poverty of Jesus Christ. I have no desire to disedify anyone."

In early December when trees and shrubs nodded beneath the snow, Mother de Chantal returned to Lyons from her visit to the two Visitation convents located in nearby cities. On the morning of the 11th, she had the happiness of a long, intimate talk with Francis and at its close, deeply moved by his intense spirituality and sincerity, she exclaimed in holy veneration, "Father, I have no doubt but that one day you will be canonized and I hope that I shall have my part in obtaining it."

"Mother," replied the holy Bishop, "God might indeed work such a miracle, but those who will deal with my canonization are yet unborn."

Prophetic words, and the last words of Francis to Jane Frances. Much as Mother de Chantal wished to remain at Lyons to profit by the saintly Bishop's counsels, she was obliged to visit other Visitation foundations and on December 12th she left for Grenoble.

On Christmas eve, Francis celebrated Mid-night Mass in the Visitation chapel. From the convent he went to the Dominican church where as Chief Almoner to the Princess Christine, he heard her and her husband's confessions, and offered the Aurora Mass in their presence, giving them Holy Communion. He then returned to the Visitation convent, intending to offer his third Mass at once. In the sacristy, however, he found the chaplain already vested so he assisted at his three Masses, offered in succession, and then said his near mid-day. After a light lunch he gave the holy habit to two postulants and preached on the epistle of the first Mass of Christmas. At the insistence of the Sisters, he took a short repose, and then discussed with them the beauty of the feast and the great love of God for mankind. Late in the afternoon he paid the Queen Mother a farewell visit, as she was leaving

Lyons the following day. It was quite late before Francis was able to leave the Court, the night had turned much colder and "'Winter, the grand old harper, smote his thunder harp of pines," playing a mournful dirge as the tired bishop made his way back to the convent grounds.

On the morning of December the 27th, as Francis was dressing he said to one of his servants, "I notice that my eyesight is failing badly. That means I have not long to live."

By sheer dint of will-power, he managed, however, to say Mass at the Convent, and visit both the Duke of Nemours and the Prince of Piedmont. When he returned to the little cottage he was utterly spent. The food and drink his servant thought would refresh him were barely touched. During the afternoon a number of friends and acquaintances, hearing that Francis was soon to leave Lyons, called to ask for his blessing. In decided contrast to his usual custom of accompanying them to the door the bishop remained seated near the fire-place. Monsieur Rolland noticed this and asked Francis whether he felt too ill to travel.

"It is late, let us not leave until tomorrow," he suggested.

Francis smiled weakly, and merely stated, "You

think I am ill," and rose from his chair and went into another room.

Monsieur Rolland, following Francis, mentioned a sermon he had lately heard preached before Queen Anne. "Among other things, my lord," remarked the priest, "the speaker urged her Majesty to love her servants."

Francis turned to his friend with his charming smile and asked, "And you, Monsieur Rolland, do you love me well?"

Canon Rolland, softly sobbing, could only nod his head in affirmation.

"It is well," said Francis slowly. "I, too, love you, my good Monsieur Rolland, but let us love God best for He is our Divine Master."

When Francis finished speaking he fainted and suffered a slight stroke of apoplexy. At length, his servants managed to get him to bed and sent for the doctors who immediately adopted harsh measures to the sick man, applying a red hot iron to his head and neck in order to arouse him. They were not effective. About one o'clock on the following morning Francis received Extreme Unction.

Great consternation prevailed when the news heart-breaking and heavy, flew from tongue to tongue, that the Bishop of Geneva was dying. Crowds hastened to the nearest churches to pray that his saintly life might be spared. Father Fourier hurried to his former pupil's bedside and asked Francis whether or not he remembered him.

The dying Bishop, his face expressive of affection and gratitude for his dear teacher whispered feebly, "If I forget thee, let my right hand be forgotten."

"Will you not say like St. Martin 'Lord, if I am still necessary to Thy people I refuse not this labor?' " pleaded the Jesuit.

Francis murmured, "I necessary? No, I am a useless servant, useless, quite useless."

With the passage of the bleak December hours Francis grew gradually weaker, frequently lapsing into drowsiness. As the early evening shadows fell and the meadowland of heaven blossomed with faint golden stars, the dying prelate turned to the Jesuit and weakly taking his hand quoted the words used centuries past by the two spent disciples of Emmaus, "It is towards evening, and the day is now far spent . . . . Jesus . . . " Francis then lost all power of speech.

Those present began the prayers for the dying and when they came to the invocation, "All ye Holy Innocents, pray for him," they repeated it thrice in honor of the day's festival, the Feast of the Holy Innocents. At the third invocation the seraphic soul of the holy Bishop left the body already radiant in death with the reflection of Beatific Glory, and winged its flight straight as an arrow to the Sacred Heart of Jesus.

"Only the actions of the just
    Smell sweet and blossom in their dust."

Is it any wonder that the fragrance of love, mingled with the perfume of the lily of purity and the violet of humility, and diffused themselves throughout the little cottage room so that all mourners were conscious of a celestial perfume that raised their minds and hearts to God?

* * *

Death took Francis when he was ready for eternal life. The glowing tribute he long ago had paid to St. Joseph, when he was talking to his Visitandine daughters, might well be repeated for his eulogy, "Behold the palm, the prince of trees, how it keeps its flowers hidden! So does the just hide his virtues under the veil of humility, until death."

With open arms and flaming heart Francis had lived joyously and generously the early morning, the noon-tide splendor and the glorious evening of his years. As Christ's ambassador he labored uncomplainingly and uncompromisingly in his gallant quest for souls. In his search, "down the days and down the years," Francis, sweet-tempered as honey, had found roses in the thorny stretches, sweetness in the bitter tasks and his God and his All in the homely virtues that bloom at the foot of the cross.

* * *

Forty-three years after his death, Francis was canonized by Pope Alexander VII who appointed January the 29th as his festal day. In 1877 Pope Pius IX proclaimed him a Doctor of the Church and in 1926, Pius XI announced the saintly Bishop of Geneva as Patron of the Universal Press.